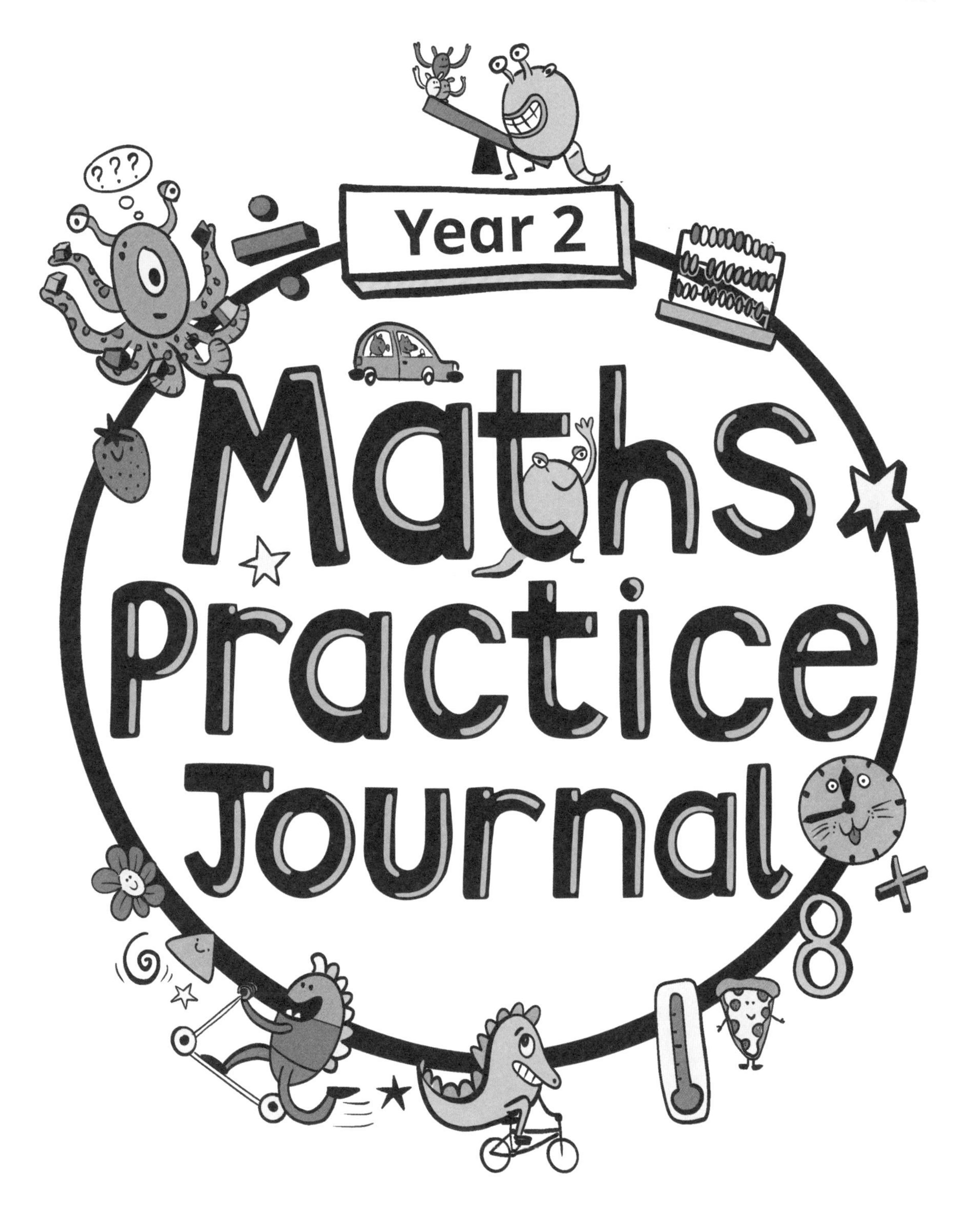

Series Editor and Author: MK Connolly

Contents

Block 1 Place value

In this block, we think about numbers in different ways.
Here are some ways we can show and talk about 13

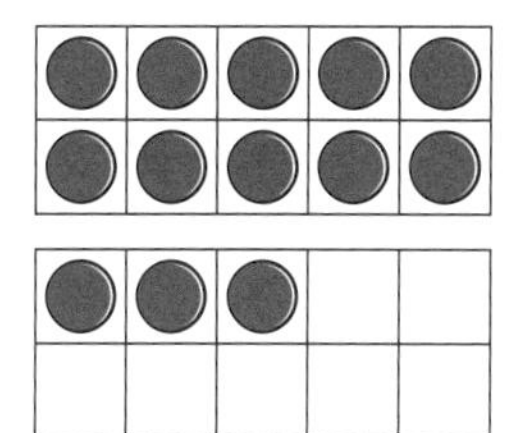

13 written as a word is **thirteen**.

Thirteen written in **numerals** is 13

13 is made up of 1 **ten** and 3 **ones**. 10 + 3 = 13

When we break numbers into smaller parts, it is called **partitioning**.
We can partition numbers into tens and ones in different ways.
We can record the partitions as number sentences.

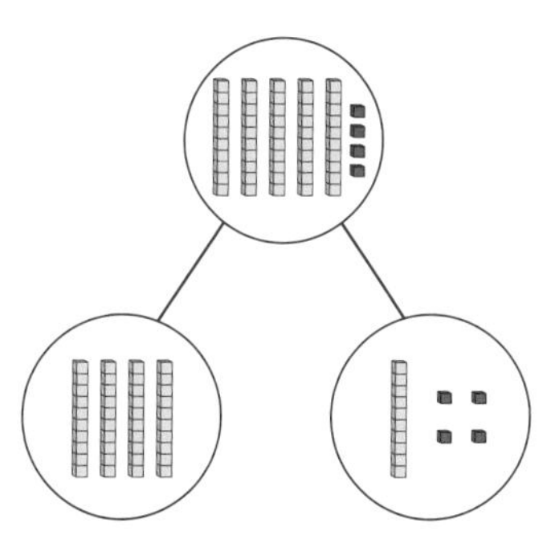

Tens	Ones

54 = 5 tens and 4 ones

54 = 50 + 4

54 = 4 tens and 14 ones

54 = 40 + 14

We think about numbers on a **number line**. The value of the **start point** is 56. This number line has 10 **intervals**.

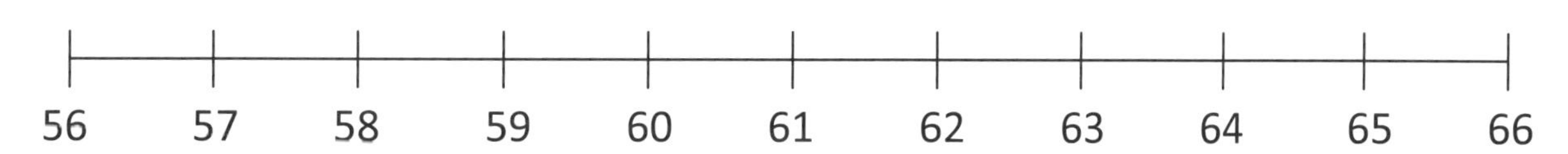

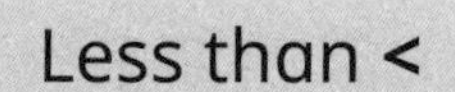

Less than <

Equal to =

Greater than >

We use these symbols to compare numbers.
The number line helps us to see that 60 > 57

Here are some maths words that we see.
What do they mean?

place value **numerals** **hundreds** **tens** **ones** **partition**
order **compare** **interval** **start point** **equal to**
greater than **less than** **estimate**

Place value

Date:

Let's practise

1 Write the numbers in numerals and words.

a) 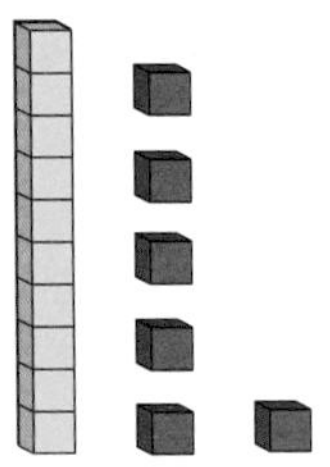

b) 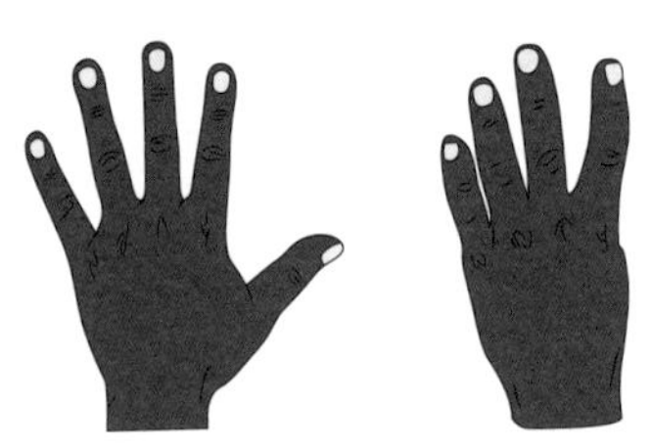

c) 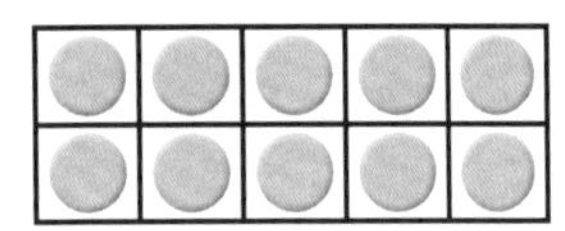 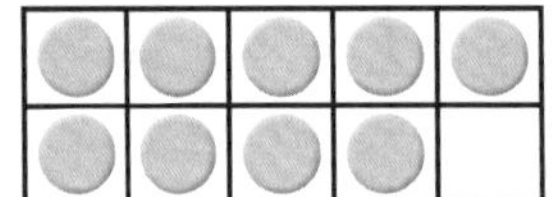 

2 How many objects are there?

a) 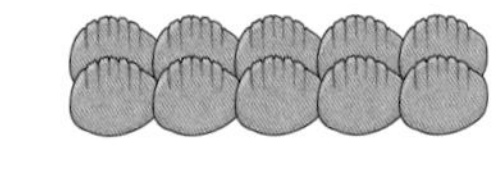 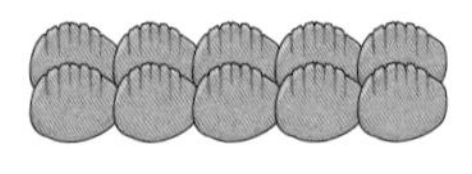 

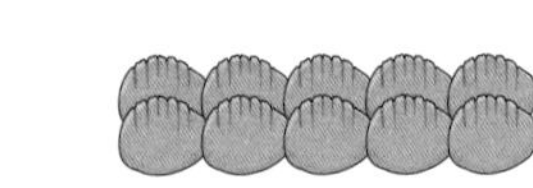 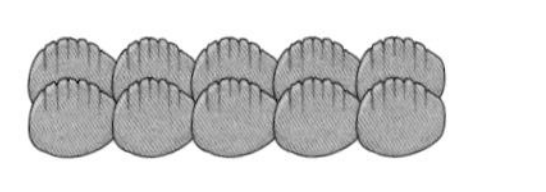 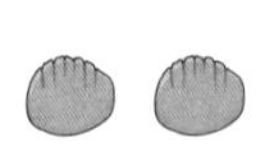

b) 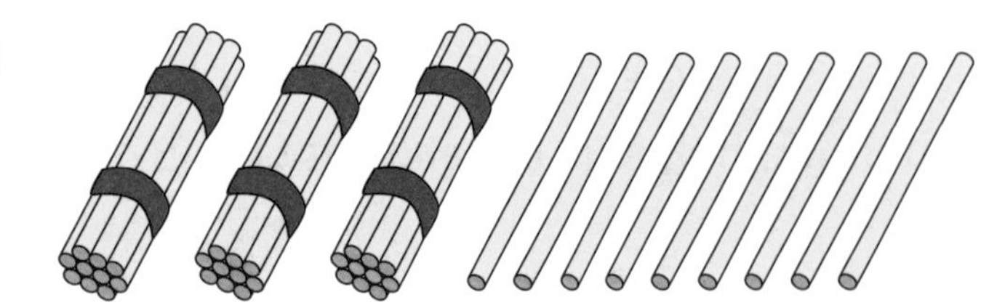 

c)   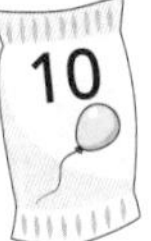  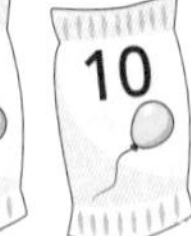

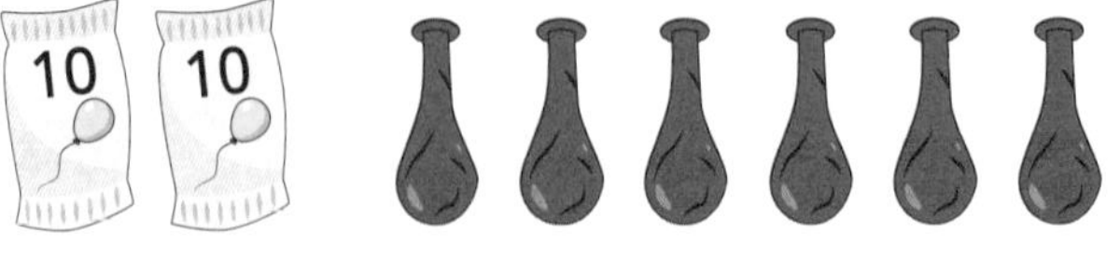 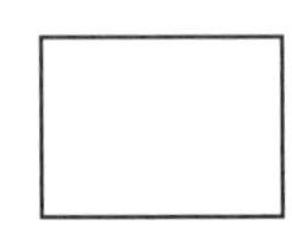

3 Tiny is counting candles.

I have 50 candles.

Do you agree with Tiny? ________

Explain your answer.

____

____

4 Complete the sentences to describe the numbers.

a)

Tens	Ones

There are ☐ tens and ☐ ones.

The number is ☐

b)

Tens	Ones
3	6

There are ☐ tens and ☐ ones.

The number is ☐

Real world maths

Put some handfuls of pasta on a table.

If you don't have pasta, use another group of small objects.

Arrange them into groups of 10

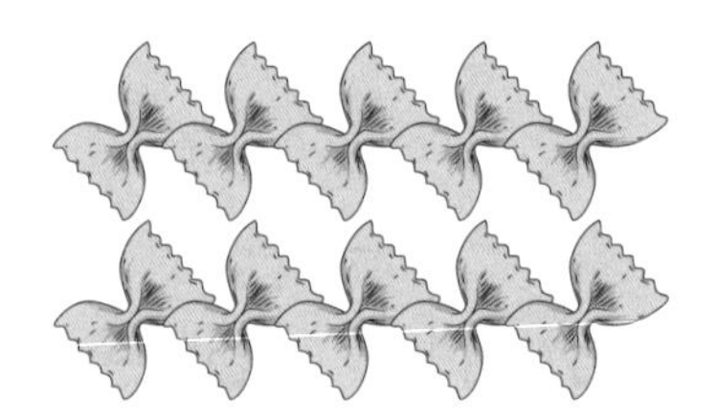

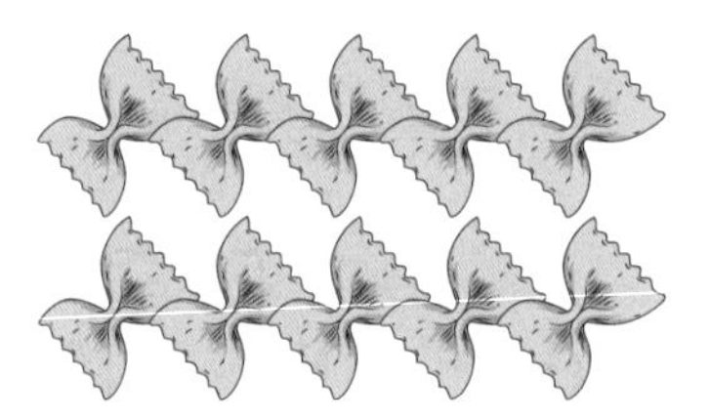

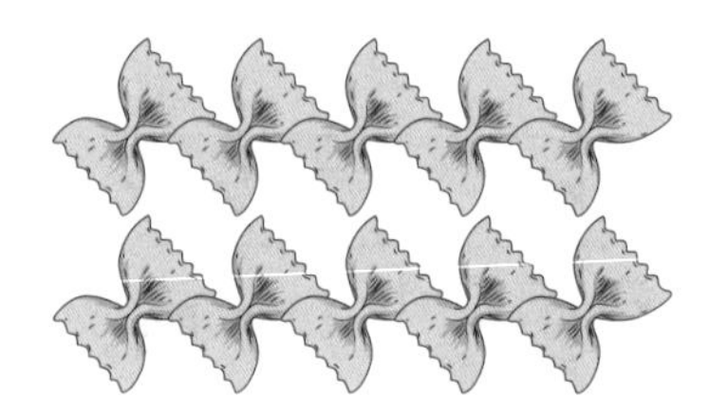

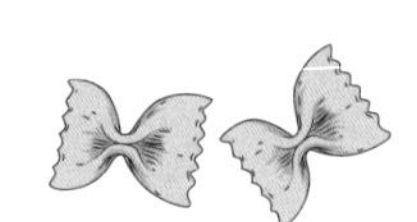

How many pieces of pasta have you got? 

How many tens are there? 

How many ones are there? 

Do you need to count each piece of pasta individually?

How many in total? 

How did you find these questions?   

Place value

Date:

Let's practise

1 Draw base 10 to complete the part-whole models.

a)

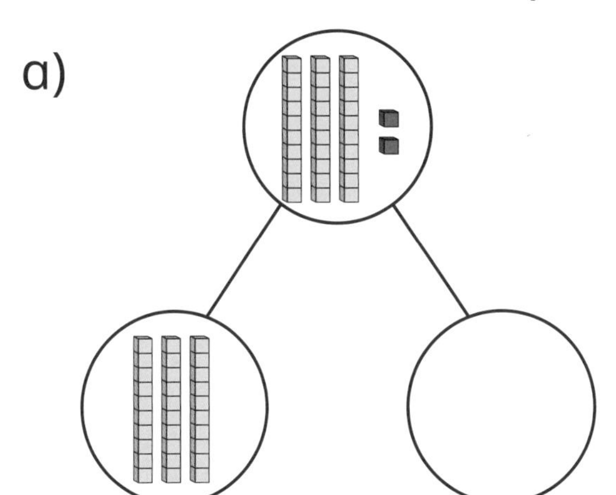

b)

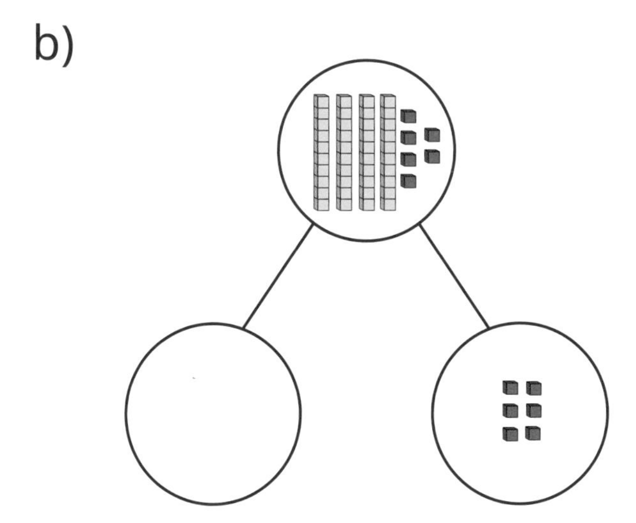

2 Complete the sentences.

a) 56 has ☐ tens and ☐ ones.

b) 73 has ☐ tens and ☐ ones.

c) 60 has ☐ tens and ☐ ones.

d) ☐ has 9 tens and 2 ones.

e) ☐ has 8 ones and 1 ten.

3 Complete the part-whole models.
Then write the missing numbers in words.

a) 28

20

____

c) 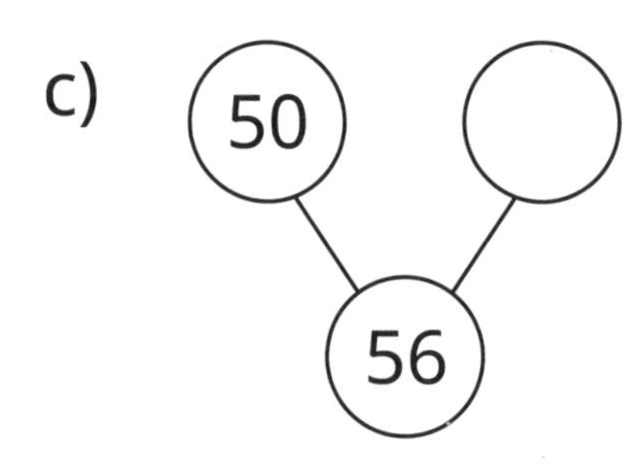

____

b) 73

3

____

d) 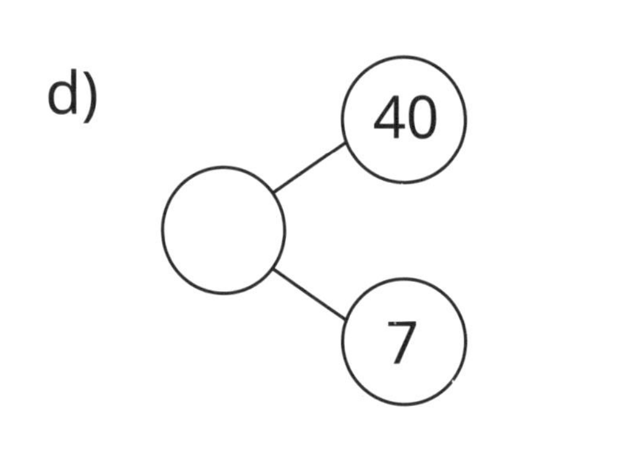

____

4 Use the base 10 to partition 48 in 4 different ways.

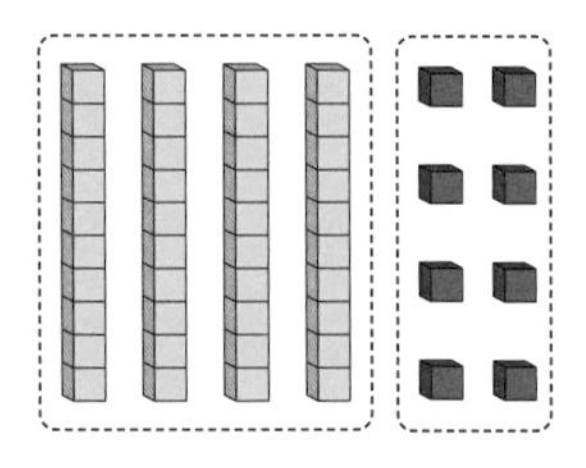

48 = ☐ + ☐

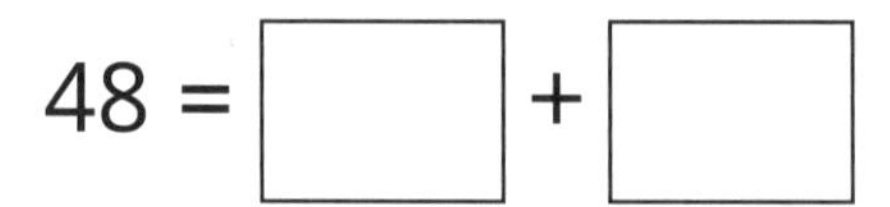

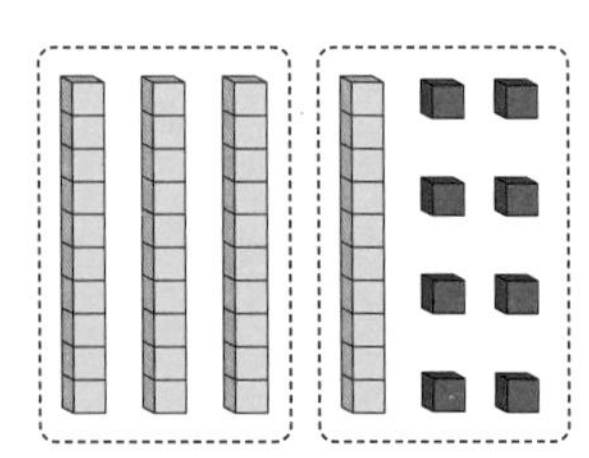

48 = ☐ + ☐

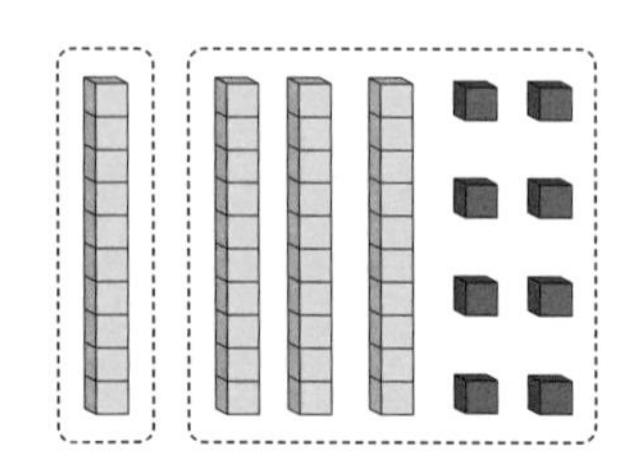

48 = ☐ + ☐

Real world maths

Hunt around your home for some 2-digit numbers.

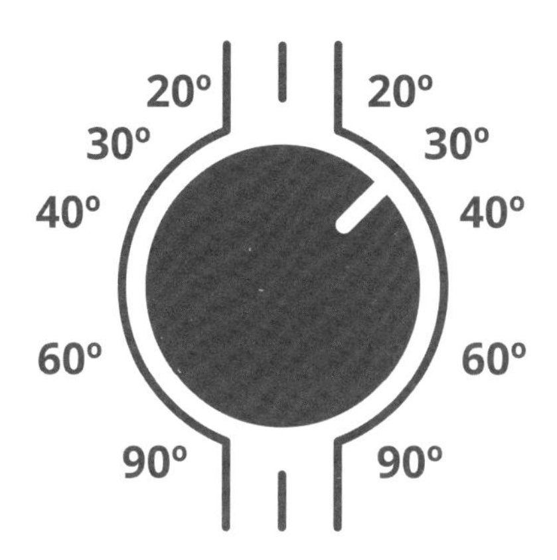

I can see numbers on my washing machine. The dial is pointing to thirty. 10 + 20 = 30
15 + 15 = 30

I can see 20 on my microwave. 10 + 10 = 20 and 15 + 5 = 20. How else can you partition the numbers?

Record the numbers you find in numerals and words.

Partition each number in 2 different ways.

My number in words is __________ and in numerals is 

☐ = ☐ + ☐   ☐ = ☐ + ☐

My number in words is __________ and in numerals is 

☐ = ☐ + ☐   ☐ = ☐ + ☐

How did you find these questions?  

Place value

Date:

Let's practise

1 What numbers are the arrows pointing to?

a)

0 100

b)

0 50

c)

0 50

2 Draw an arrow to show the position of each number on the number line.

a) 23

20 30

b) 78

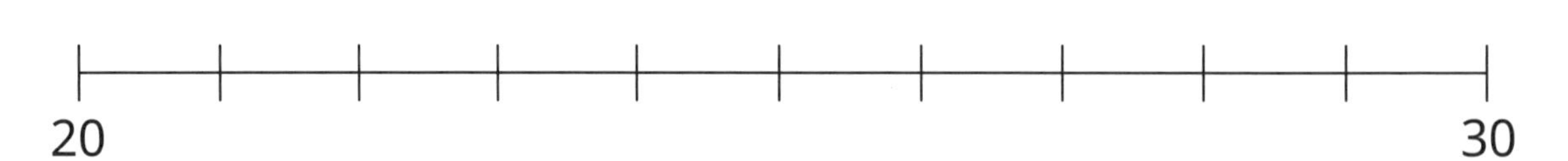

70 80

c) 95

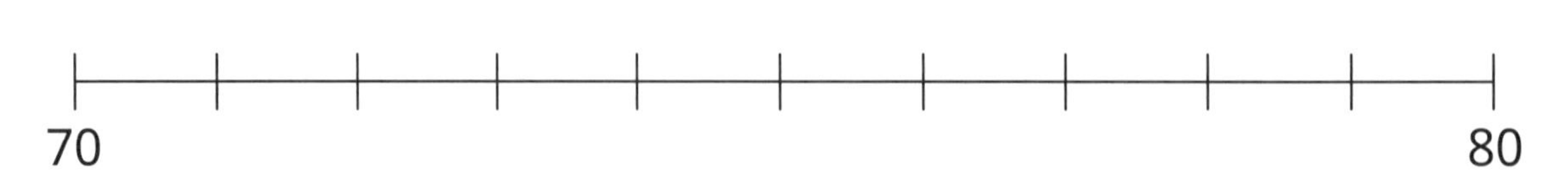

90 100

3 Estimate the numbers the arrows are pointing to.

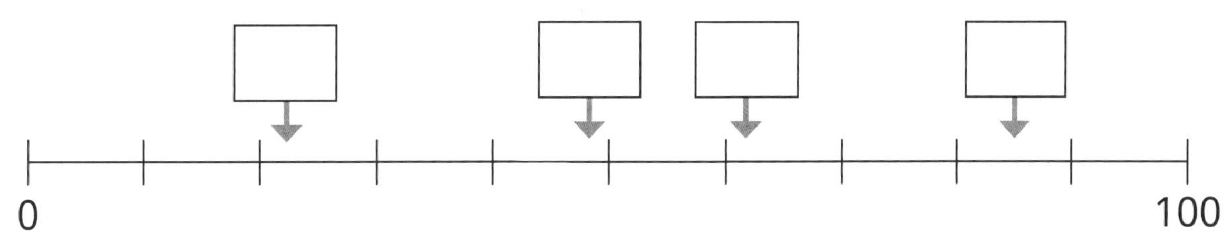

When we **estimate**, we make a reasonable guess.

4 Max has these sweets.

Jo has these sweets.

Who has more sweets? ____________

How do you know?

____

____

5 Kim is thinking of a number.

What number could Kim be thinking of?

[ ]

My number has 4 tens and more than 7 ones.

Think it out

Here are 2 number lines.
The shapes have the same value on both number lines.

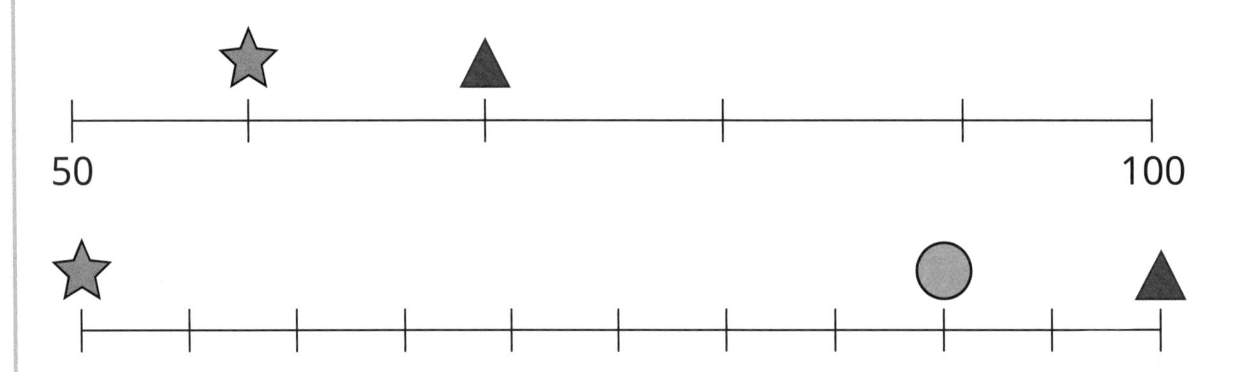

Draw an arrow to estimate the position of the circle on this number line.

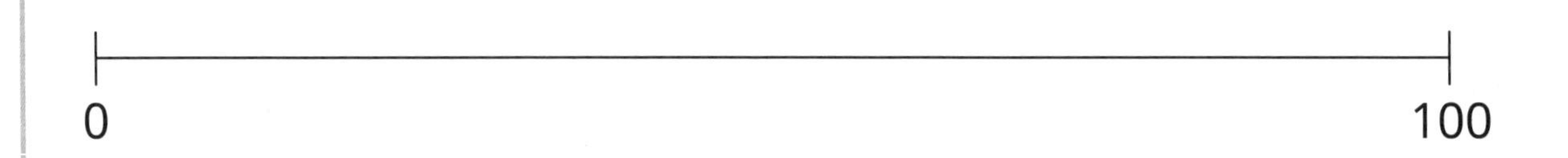

Real world maths

Make your own number line, like this.
Use card, string and pegs.

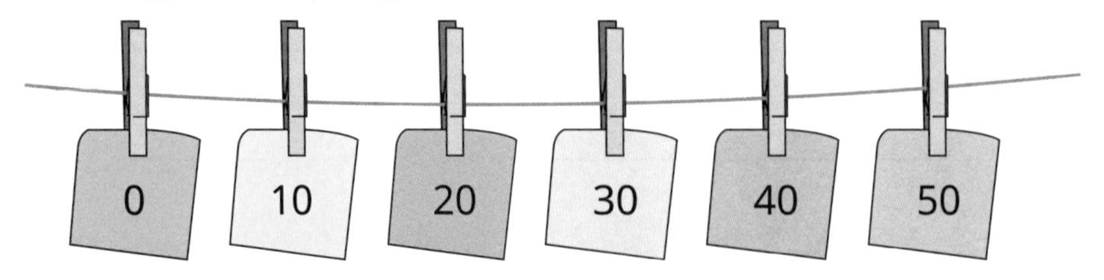

Point to a spot between 2 cards on your number line.
Ask an adult to estimate what number you are pointing to.

How did they work it out?

How did you find these questions?   

Place value

Date:

Let's practise

1 Use **less than**, **greater than** or **equal to** to complete the sentences.

a) 15 is ______________________ 20

b) 63 is ______________________ 57

c) Eighty is ______________________ eighteen

d) Fifty-four is ______________________ 54

2 Use <, > or = to compare the numbers.

a) 29 ◯ 25

b) 37 ◯ 87

c) 40 + 9 ◯ 40 + 1

d) 40 + 3 ◯ 30 + 13

3 Draw arrows to estimate the position of each number on the number line.

46 92 31 75

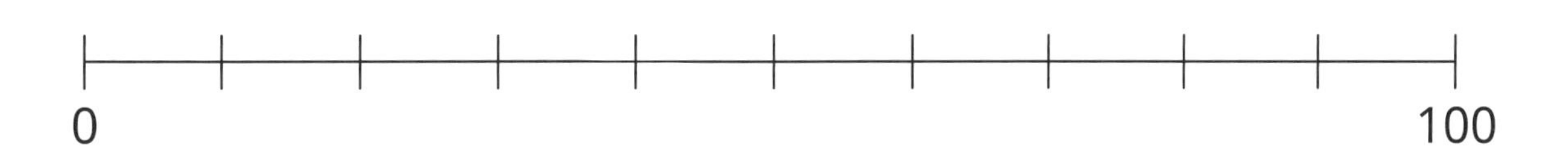

Write the numbers in order, starting with the smallest.

☐ ☐ ☐ ☐

4 How many are there?

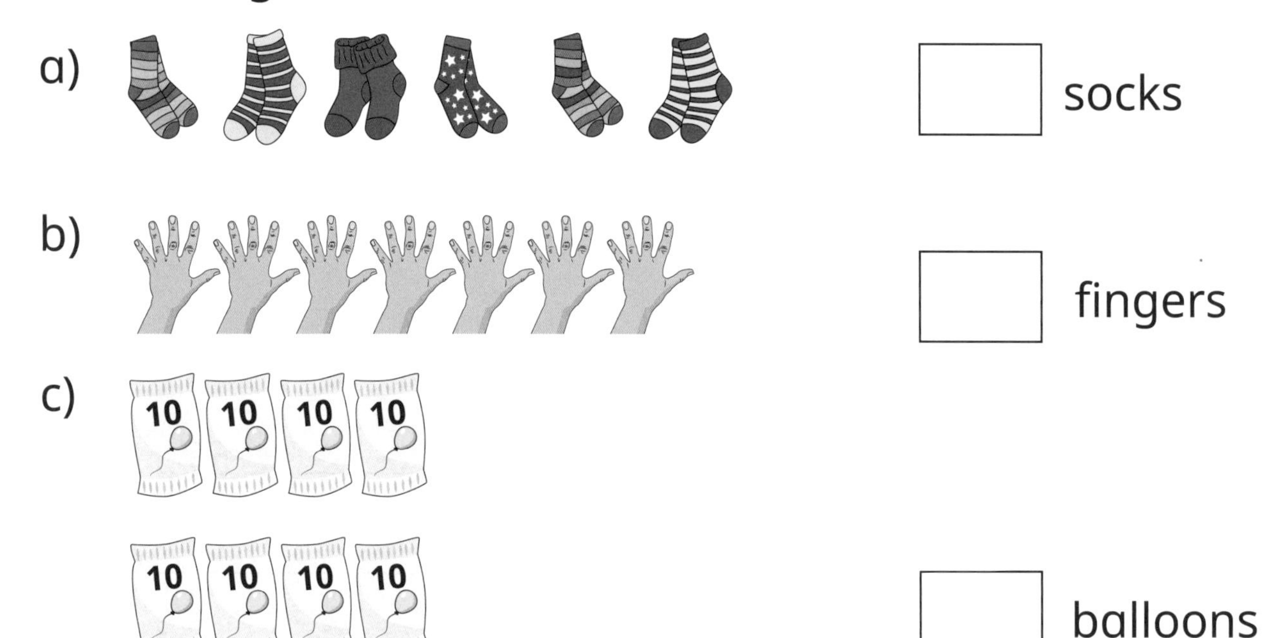

5 How many wheels are there in total?

6 Biscuits come in packets of 2, 5 and 10

Ben buys 3 packs of 2 biscuits.

Ann buys 3 packs of 5 biscuits.

Kay buys 3 packs of 10 biscuits.

How many biscuits do they have in total? ☐

Think it out

Complete the number tracks.

0	2	4							

0	5	10							

0	10	20							

What numbers are on all 3 number tracks? ______________

If the number tracks carried on, what other numbers would be in all 3 number tracks? ______________________

What do you notice?

Do you notice any patterns in the number tracks? Describe them.

____

____

Complete this number track.

0	3	6							

What number, other than 0, would appear on all 4 number tracks if they carried on?

☐

How did you find these questions?   

Autumn term

Block 2 Addition and subtraction

In this block, we use **number bonds to 10** to **add** and **subtract** with 1-digit and 2-digit numbers.
Here are 4 number bonds to 10

$4 + 6 = 10$ $2 + 8 = 10$ $3 + 7 = 10$ $1 + 9 = 10$

When we add three 1-digit numbers, we can add two of the numbers and add the third number to the answer.
Using number bonds to 10 can help with additions like $3 + 6 + 7$

$3 + 7 + 6$

$10 + 6 = 16$

So, $3 + 6 + 7 = 16$

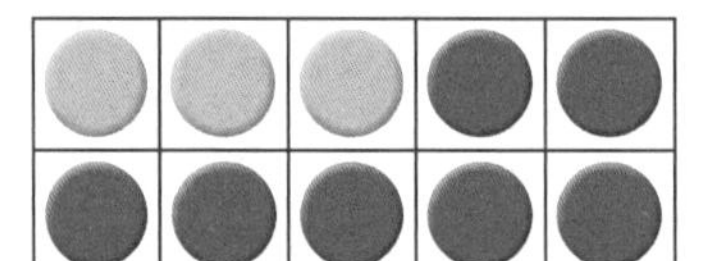

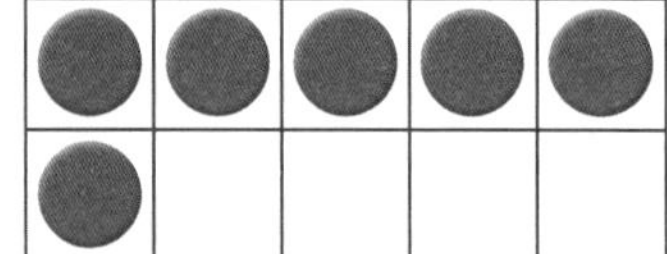

We use number bonds to add by making 10 and adding to or across the next 10

$35 + 8 = 35 + 5 + 3$

$40 + 3 = 43$

So, $35 + 8 = 43$

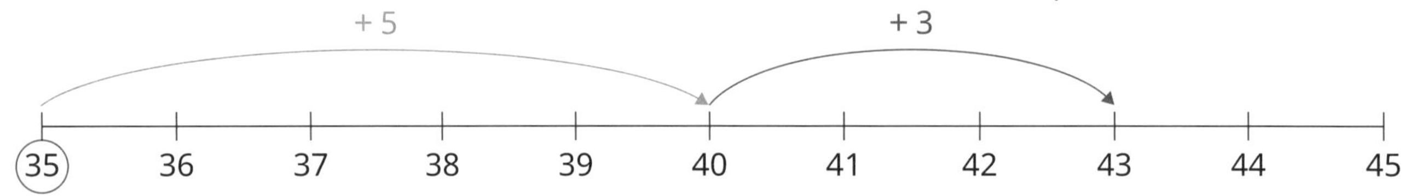

Sometimes when we subtract from 2-digit numbers, there will not be enough **ones**, so we need to **exchange**.

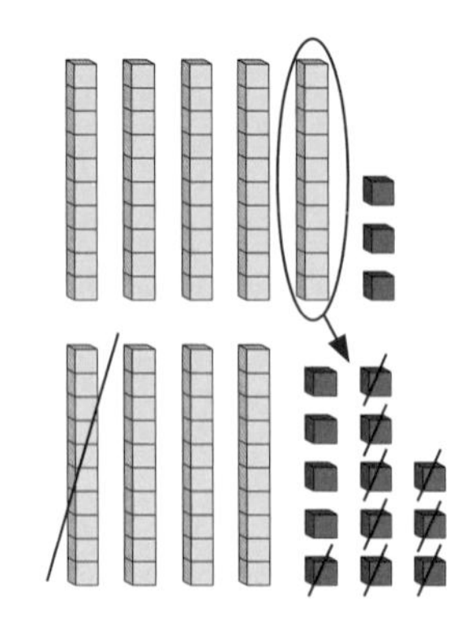

$53 - 19 = ?$

First, I make 53 with base ten.

Next, I exchange 1 ten for 10 ones.

Then, I subtract the 9 ones.

Finally, I subtract the 1 ten.

I now have 3 tens and 4 ones.

$53 - 19 = 34$

Here are some maths words that we see. What do they mean?

tens **ones** **partition** **exchange** **multiples of 10**
number bonds **add** **subtract** **take away**

Addition and subtraction

Date:

Let's practise

1 Complete the number bonds.

a) 3 + ☐ = 10 13 + ☐ = 20

☐ + 2 = 10 ☐ + 2 = 20

10 = 5 + ☐ 20 = 15 + ☐

10 = 0 + ☐ 20 = 0 + ☐

2 Complete the part-whole model.

Then complete the number sentences to match the part-whole model.

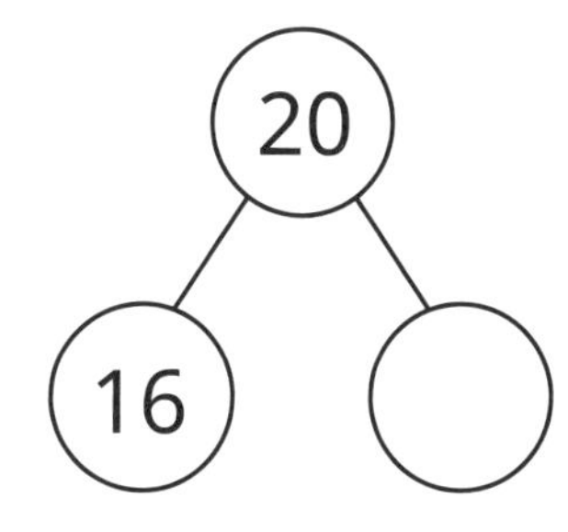

☐ + ☐ = ☐

☐ + ☐ = ☐

☐ – ☐ = ☐

☐ – ☐ = ☐

3 How many balloons are there?

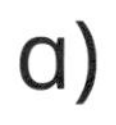

a) ☐

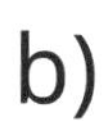

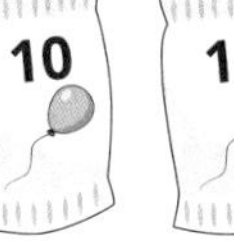

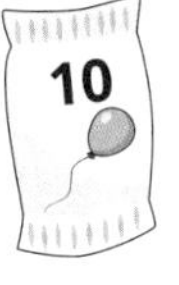

b) ☐

What do you notice? What is the same? What is different?

4 Complete the number sentences.

a) $2 + 4 = \square$

$20 + 40 = \square$

d) $9 = 7 + \square$

$90 = 70 + \square$

b) $1 + 8 = \square$

$10 + 80 = \square$

e) $7 - 3 = \square$

$70 - 30 = \square$

c) $3 + \square = 10$

$30 + \square = 100$

f) $\square = 8 - 2$

$\square = 80 - 20$

5 A shop has 100 red and green apples in total.
Here are the red apples.

How many green apples does the shop have? $\square$

Talk it out

Write all the number bonds to 10

Write all the number bonds to 100 using tens.

What do you notice?
Tell someone in your home.

I noticed that the number bonds to 10 . . .

I noticed that the number bonds to 100 . . .

How did you find these questions?   

Addition and subtraction

Date:

Let's practise

1 Complete the additions.

a) 42 + 5 = ☐

b) 56 = 54 + ☐

2 Complete the subtractions.

a) 47 – 3 = ☐

b) ☐ – 5 = 81

c) 63 – 3 = ☐

d) ☐ = 29 – 5

3 Complete the additions.

a)

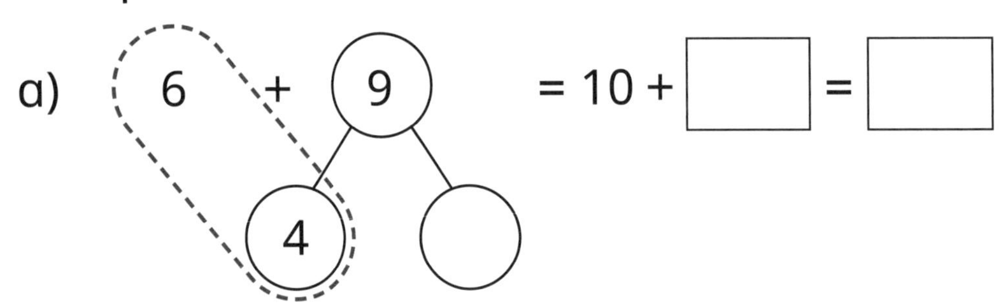

b)

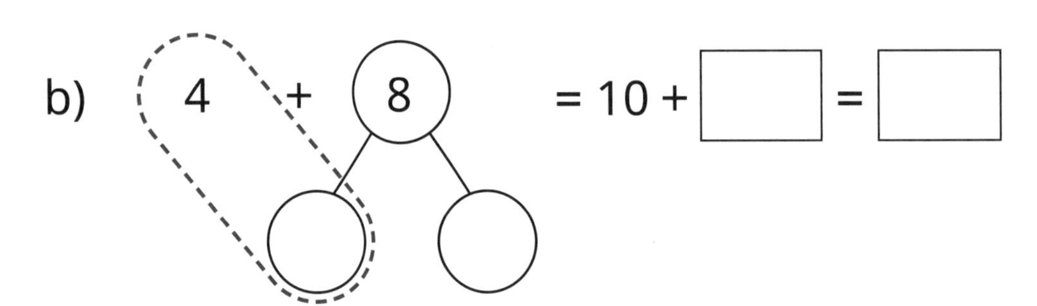

c) 7 + 5 = ☐ + ☐ = ☐

How does partitioning one of the numbers help?

4 Tiny is working out 8 + 3

8, 9, 10
The answer is 10

Do you agree with Tiny? ________

Explain your answer.

____

5 Complete the additions.

Does it matter in what order you add the numbers?

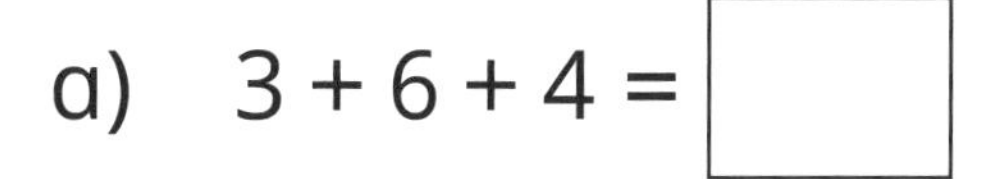

a) 3 + 6 + 4 = ☐

b) 2 + 8 + 5 = ☐

c) 8 + 9 + 1 = ☐

6 Complete the additions.

a) 2 + ☐ = 10

b) 12 + ☐ = 20

c) 22 + ☐ = 30

d) 32 + ☐ = 40

e) 92 + ☐ = 100

What do you notice?

7 Ben has 24 stickers.

Dan has 30 stickers.

How many more stickers does Dan have than Ben? ☐

Think it out

Roll a dice 3 times.

Add together the 3 rolls.

Look for number bonds to 10 in the calculation.

How did you add them?

What's the greatest total you can make rolling 3 dice?

What's the smallest total you can make rolling 3 dice?

How many combinations of 3 rolls can you list which have a total that crosses 10?

How did you find these questions?   

Addition and subtraction

Date:

Let's practise

1 Complete the additions.

a) 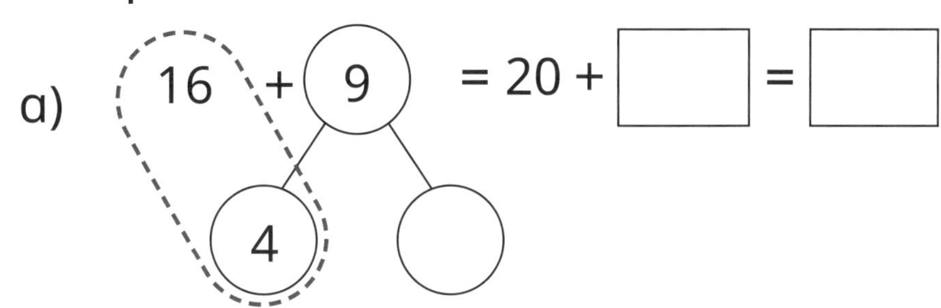

= 20 + ☐ = ☐

b) 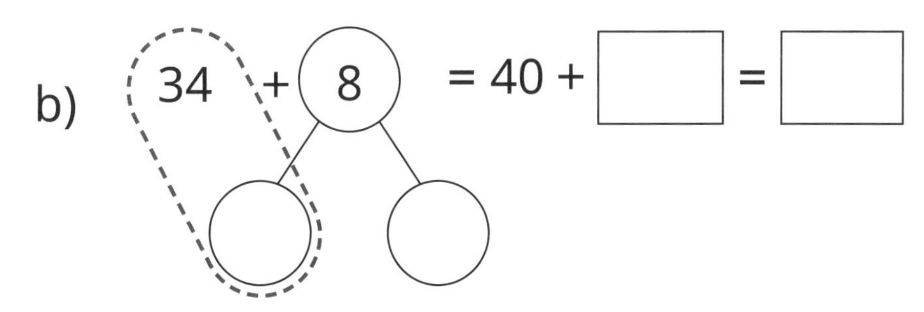

= 40 + ☐ = ☐

2 Complete the subtractions.

a) 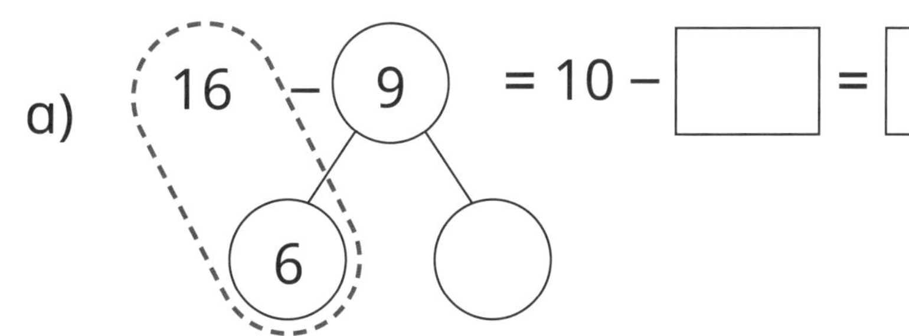

= 10 – ☐ = ☐

How many more do you need to subtract?

b) 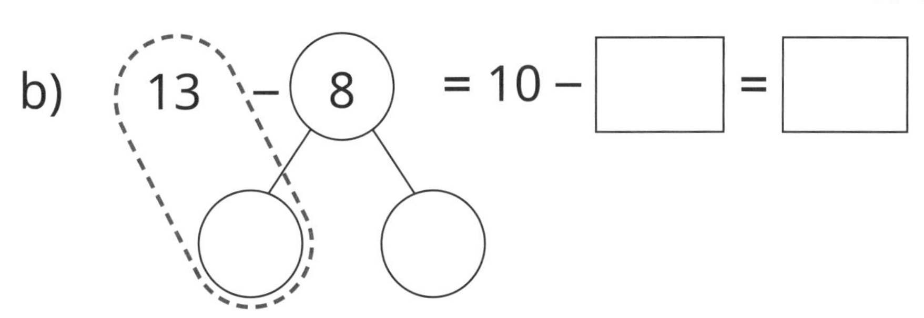

= 10 – ☐ = ☐

c) 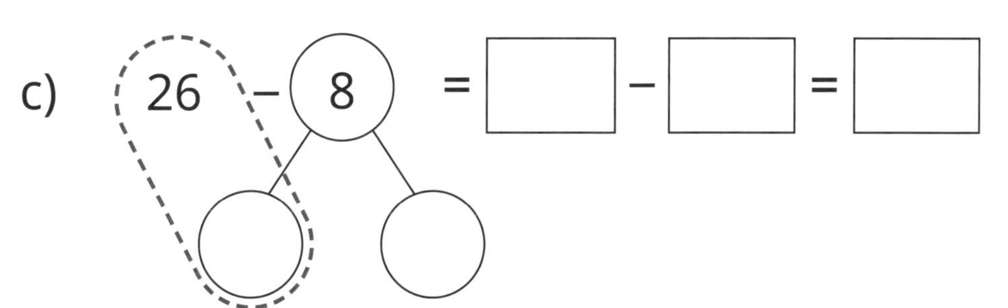

= ☐ – ☐ = ☐

3 Complete the subtractions.

a) 10 – 7 = ☐

b) 20 – 7 = ☐

c) 30 – 7 = ☐

d) 40 – 7 = ☐

e) Work out 100 – 7 = ☐

What do you notice?

4 Complete the subtractions.

a) 23 – 8 = ☐

b) 32 – 6 = ☐

c) 47 – 9 = ☐

d) 53 – 4 = ☐

e) 91 – 2 = ☐

f) 17 – 7 = ☐

g) 23 – 5 = ☐

h) 61 – 3 = ☐

How many do you need to subtract to get to the previous 10?

5 Tiny is subtracting 7 from 32

7 minus 2 is equal to 5, so the answer is 35

Do you agree with Tiny? ______________

Explain your answer.

____

____

Think it out

Here are some digit cards.

2	5	8	6	9

Choose 3 of the cards to write a subtraction.

☐☐ – ☐

Work out the answer to your subtraction. ☐

How can number bonds help you to work out the answer?

What is the greatest answer you can get using your 3 cards? ☐

What is the smallest answer you can get using your 3 cards? ☐

Swap your cards around to work it out.

How did you find these questions?  

Addition and subtraction

Date:

Let's practise

1 Max has these balloons.

He buys 3 more bags of balloons.

How many balloons does he have now? 

2 Annie has these marbles.

10 10 10 10 10 10 10

She gives 2 boxes of marbles to her friend.

How many marbles does she have left? ☐

3 Complete the calculations.

a) 42 + 20 = ☐

b) 30 + 62 = ☐

c) 75 – 20 = ☐

d) 62 – 50 = ☐

What do you notice about the number of tens? What do you notice about the number of ones?

e) 31 + ☐ = 41

f) 92 – ☐ = 72

g) 42 + 30 = 82 – ☐

h) 78 – 30 = 8 + ☐

4 Ron and Mo each have some sweets.

How many sweets do they have altogether? ☐

5 Kim and Jo each have some sweets.

How many sweets do they have altogether? ☐

6 Complete the calculations.

a) 23 + 31 = ☐

b) 38 + 13 = ☐

c) 42 + 25 = ☐

d) ☐ = 51 + 29

e) ☐ = 36 + 25

f) 22 + 49 = ☐

Do you need to make an exchange?

Think it out

Mo and Sam each have some stickers.

Mo

I have 4 sheets of 10 stickers and 3 single stickers.

If I had 3 more stickers, we would have 100 stickers in total.

Sam

How many stickers does Sam have? ☐

Show your workings.

Talk it out

How can you tell if an addition will cross a ten?

Explain to someone in your home.

Show them with examples.

There are ____ ones, so I do/do not need to make an exchange.

How did you find these questions?   

Addition and subtraction

Date:

Let's practise

How many tens and ones do you need to cross out?

1 Cross out base 10 to show the subtractions.

a) 47 – 23 =

c) 59 – 45 =

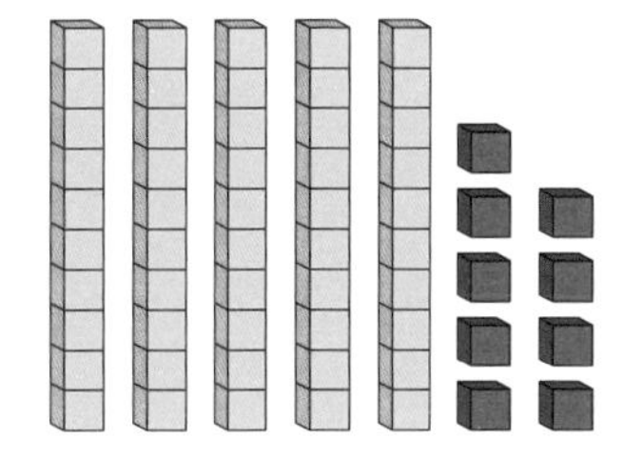

b) 72 – 51 =

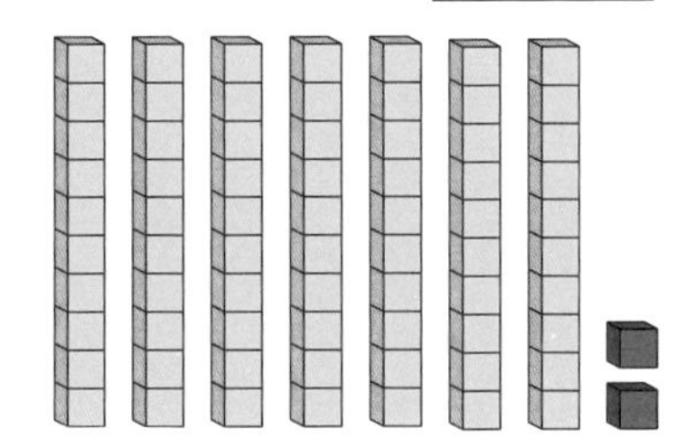

d) 28 – 17 =

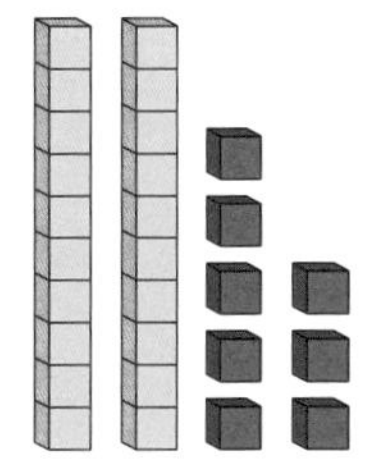

2 Jo and Kim have each made a number.

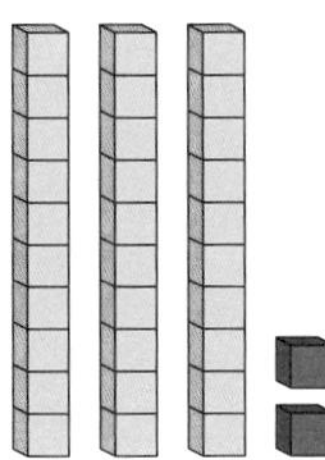

What is the same? What is different?

a) What number have they both made?

b) What is 14 less than their number?

3 Complete the subtractions.

a) 42 – 15 =

d) 72 – 47 =

b) 24 – 17 =

e) = 51 – 33

c) 56 – 27 =

f) = 92 – 78

4 Tiny has worked out the difference between 76 and 28

a) The difference is 52

Explain the mistake Tiny has made.

____

b) Work out the difference between 76 and 28 ☐

5 Complete the calculations.

a) $23 + 38 =$ ☐

b) $42 - 19 =$ ☐

c) $56 - 9 =$ ☐

d) $28 + 8 =$ ☐

e) $47 + 51 =$ ☐

f) $87 - 39 =$ ☐

g) $76 - 41 =$ ☐

h) $23 + 48 - 31 =$ ☐

6 Ron, Kim and Mo each have some buttons.

Ron has 42 buttons.

Kim has 8 fewer buttons than Ron.

Altogether, they have 100 buttons.

How many more buttons does Ron have than Mo?

How can you check your answer?

Think it out

Write a word problem for each calculation.

42 + 39

____

____

63 – 27

____

____

Ask an adult to work out the answer to your questions.

Check if they are correct.

Talk it out

Which addition has the greater answer?

38 + 45 27 + 38

How did you decide?

Did you need to work them out?

I think ... has the greatest answer because ...

I did/did not need to work them out because ...

How did you find these questions?   

Block 3 Shape

In this block, we explore **2-D** and **3-D shapes** and learn about their **properties**. 2-D shapes are **closed**, **flat** shapes. 3-D shapes are **solid** shapes that have length, width and height.

We can name and describe the properties of 2-D shapes.
This hexagon has 6 **sides** and 6 **vertices**.

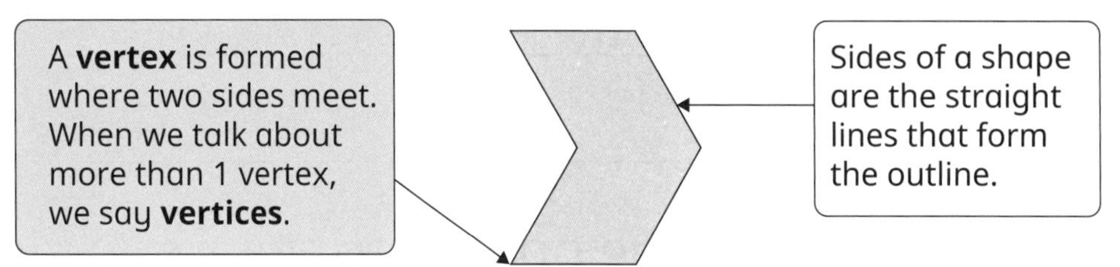

Some 2-D shapes have a **line of symmetry**. A line of symmetry divides a shape so that both sides are the same. This pentagon has a **vertical** line of symmetry.

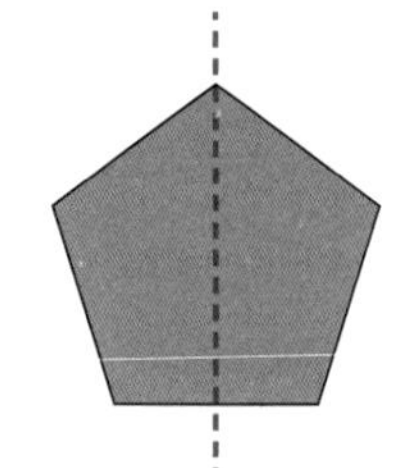

We name and describe the properties of 3-D shapes.
The **triangular prism** has 5 **faces**, 9 **edges** and 6 **vertices**.
A cylinder has 2 flat **faces**, 1 **curved surface**, 2 **edges** and 0 **vertices**.

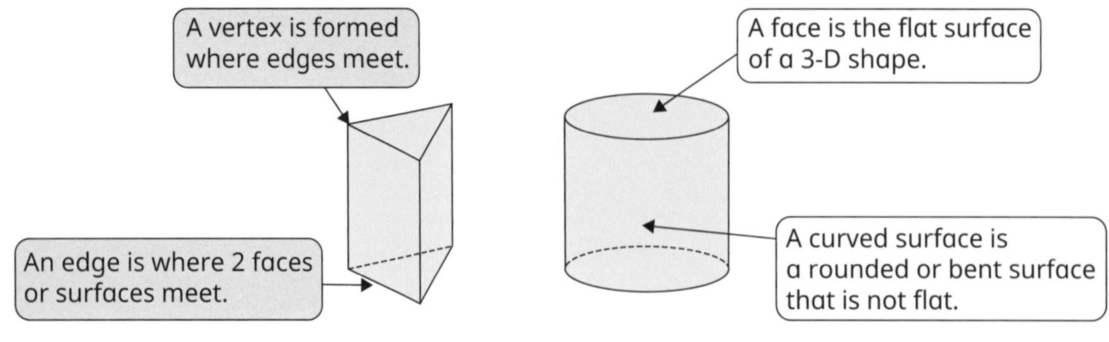

Here are some maths words that we see. What do they mean?

side **vertex** **vertices** **mirror line** **vertical line of symmetry**
closed **face** **edge** **curved surface** **pattern** **property**

Shape

Date:

Let's practise

1 Tick the shape that is the odd one out.

 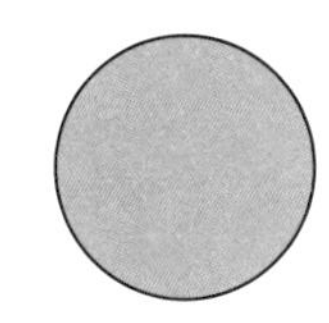 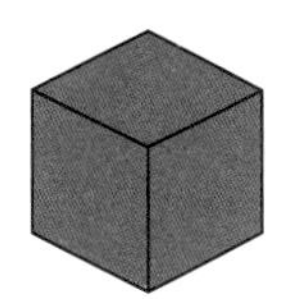 

Explain your choice.

____

2 Write the mathematical name of each shape.

a) 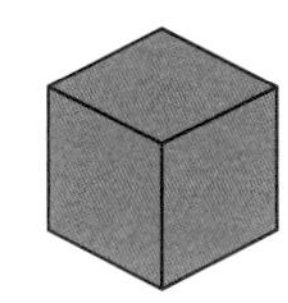

____

b) 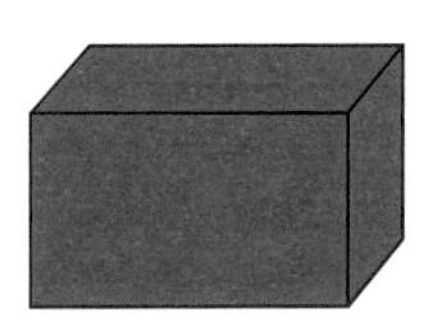

____

c) 

____

3 Write the mathematical name of each shape.

Then write how many sides and vertices each shape has.

a) 

____

sides ☐ vertices ☐

c) 

____

sides ☐ vertices ☐

b) 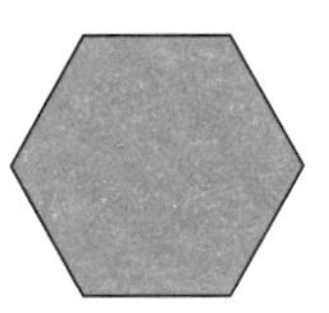

____

sides ☐ vertices ☐

d) 

____

sides ☐ vertices ☐

4 Draw a shape that has 5 sides.

5 Draw a shape that has 4 vertices.

A **vertex** is where 2 sides meet. **Vertices** means more than 1 vertex.

6 I have drawn a triangle.

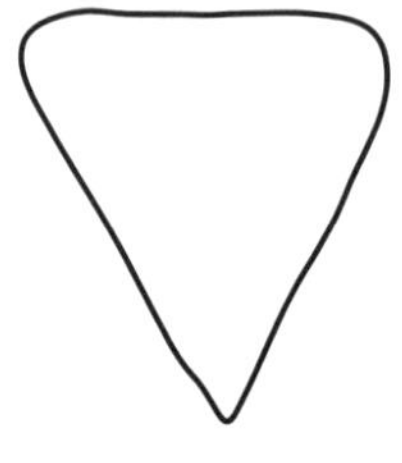

Do you agree with Tiny? ________

Explain your answer. ______________________________

____

Real world maths

Go on a 2-D shape hunt around your home.

How many of each shape can you find?

Draw them.

Shape	Draw it	How many sides?	How many vertices?	How many did you find?
Triangle				
Square				
Rectangle				
Pentagon				
Hexagon				

Did you find any other 2-D shapes?

How did you find these questions?   

Shape

Date:

Let's practise

1 Draw the vertical line of symmetry on each shape.

a) 

b) 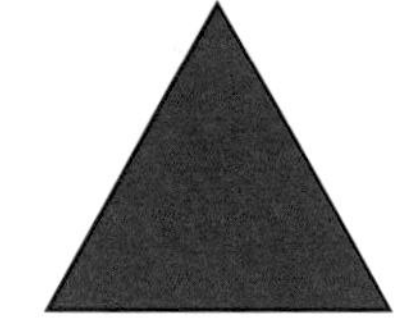

c) 

d) 

e) 

f) 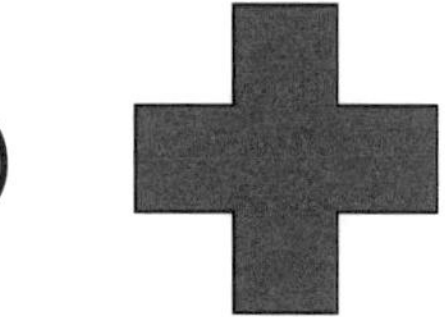

2 Use the lines of symmetry to complete the shapes.

a) 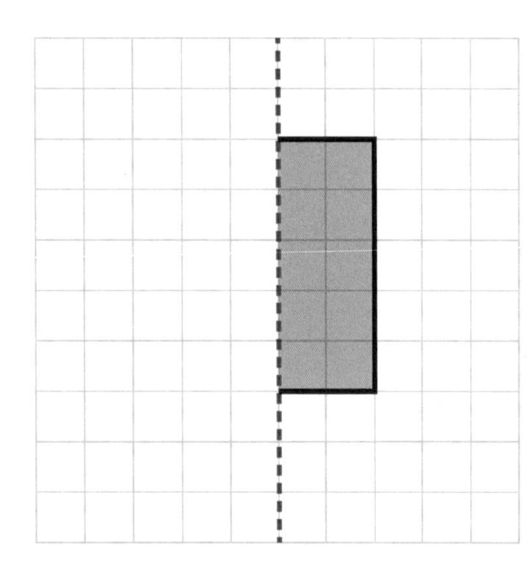

c) 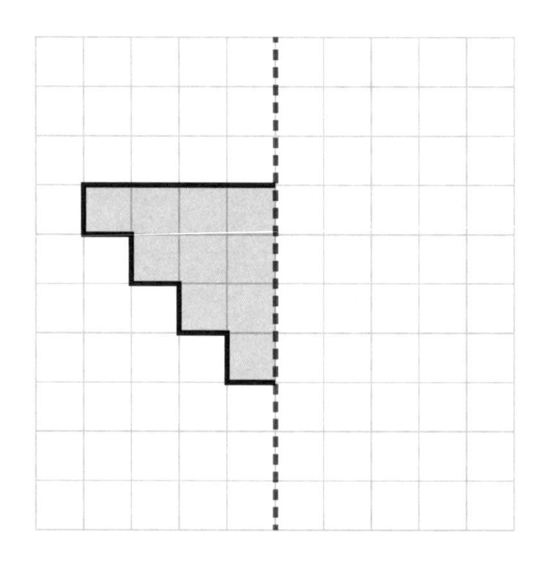

b) 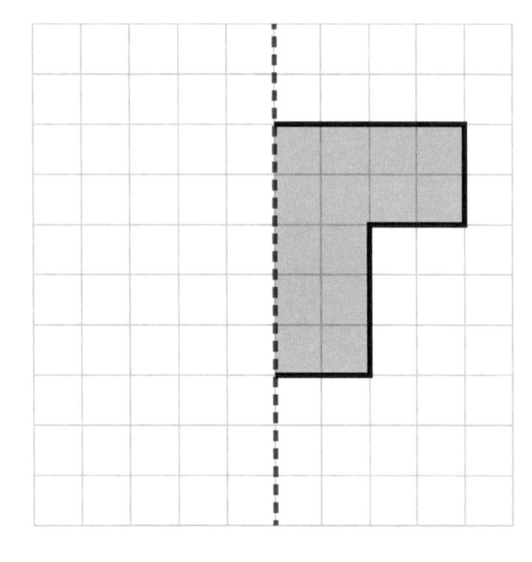

d) 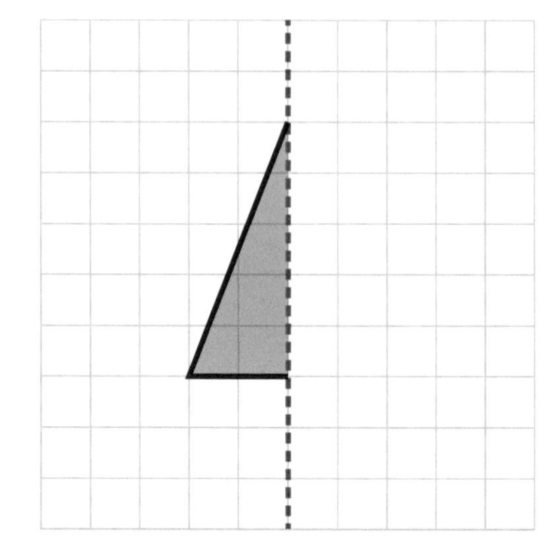

3 Here are some shapes.

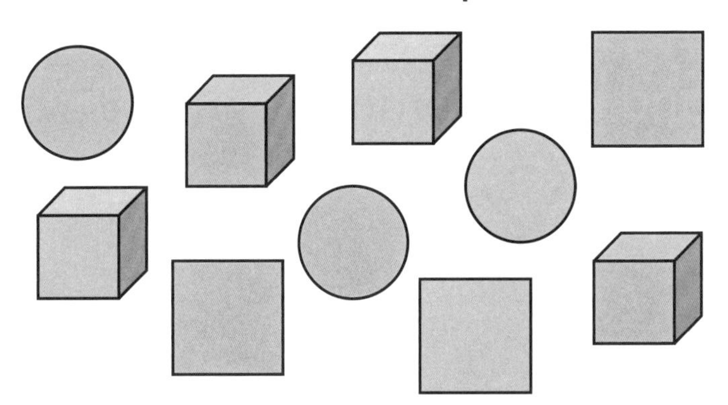

How could you sort them into 2 groups?

____

4 How many faces does each shape have?

a) 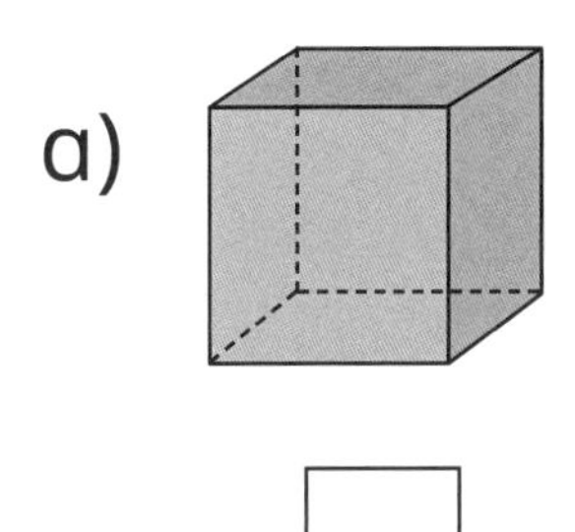

b) 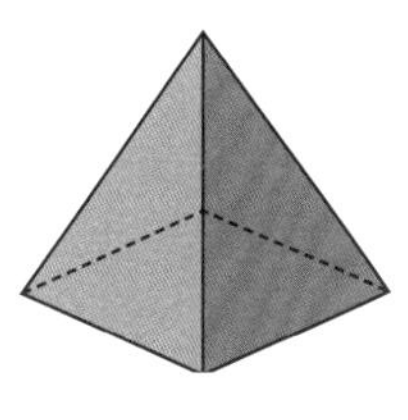

c) 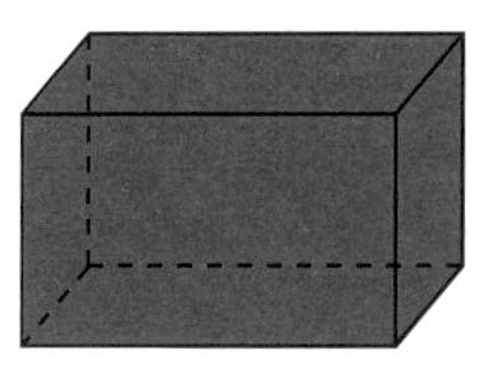

5 Max is describing a 2-D shape.

My shape has
5 sides, 5 vertices
and a vertical line
of symmetry.

Draw on the grid what Max's shape could be.

Real world maths

Find some 2-D shapes around your home that have a vertical line of symmetry.

Draw them on the grid.

Think it out

Jo is describing a 3-D shape.

What shape could Jo be describing?

____

My shape has a curved surface.

What is the difference between a face and a curved surface?

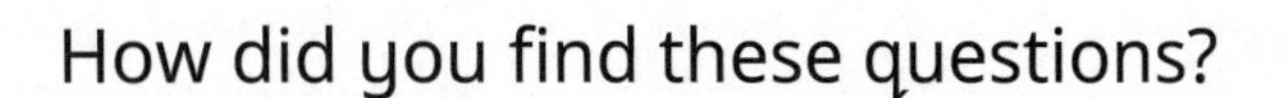
How did you find these questions?

Shape

Date:

Let's practise

1 Write the mathematical name of each 3-D shape. Then write how many faces, edges and vertices each shape has.

a) 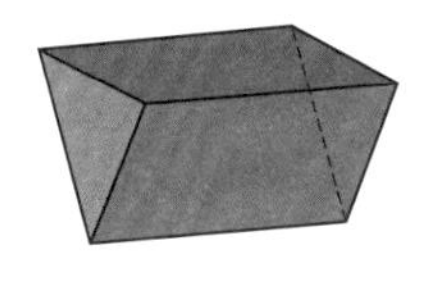

____

faces ☐

edges ☐

vertices ☐

b) 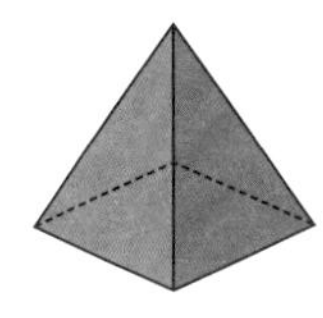

____

faces ☐

edges ☐

vertices ☐

2 Here is a shape.

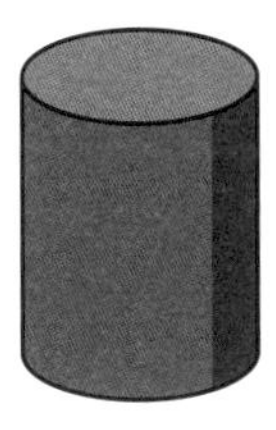

a) What is the mathematical name of the shape?

____

b) How many faces? 

c) How many curved surfaces? ☐

3 Ron is describing a 3-D shape.

My shape has zero faces, one curved surface, zero edges and zero vertices.

What shape is Ron describing?

____

4 Draw the next two shapes in each pattern.

a) 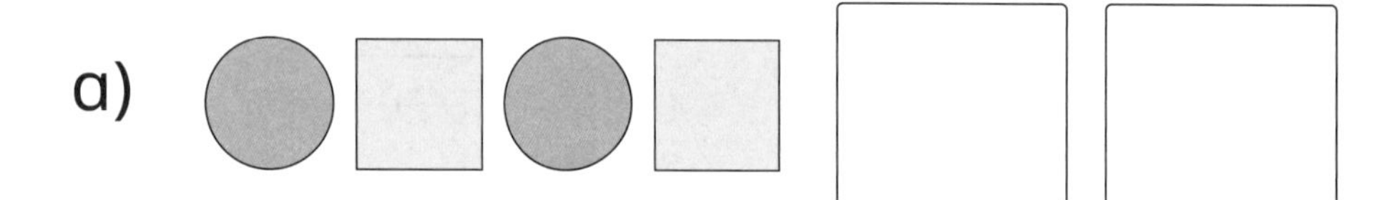

b) 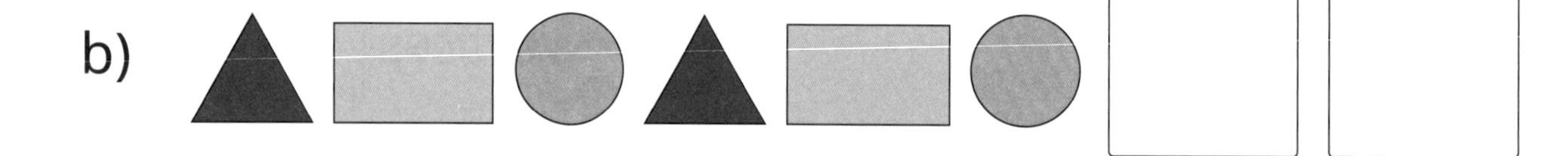

c) 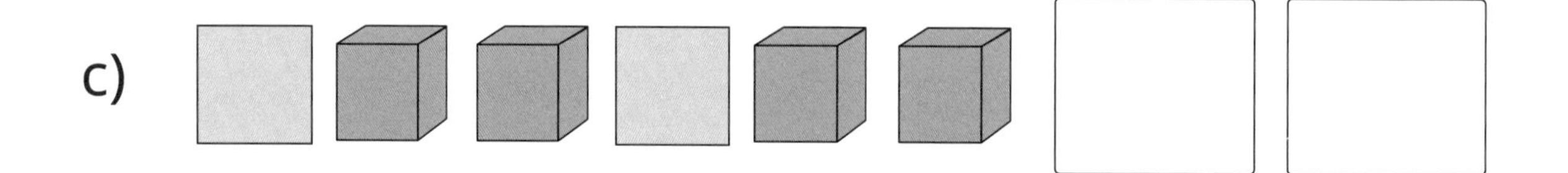

5 Complete the symmetrical patterns.

a) 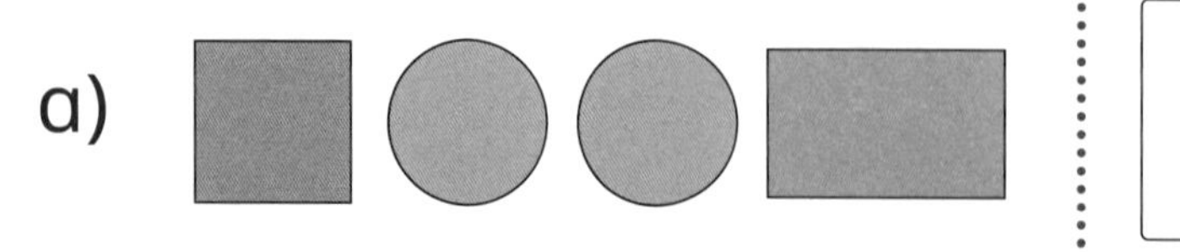

b) 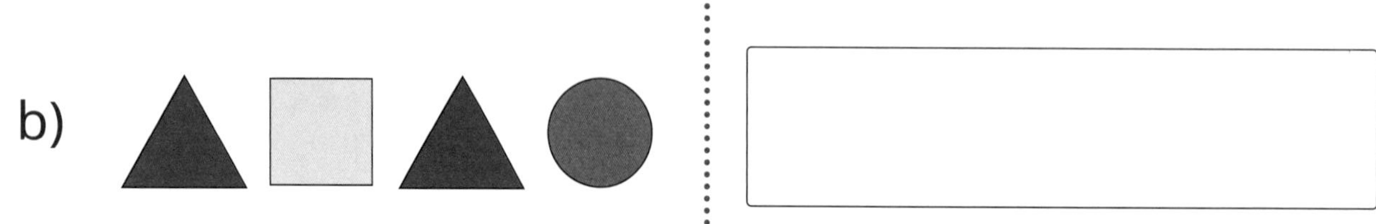

Talk it out

Find some examples of 3-D shapes around your home.

cube	☐
cuboid	☐
sphere	☐
cone	☐
cylinder	☐
pyramid	☐

Describe them to someone.

This shape is a …
It has … faces, … edges and … vertices.

I can see that face on this 3-D shape is the 2-D shape …

Real world maths

Use paint and the faces of some 3-D shapes to make shape print patterns.

Ask an adult to help you.

What different patterns can you make?

Is your pattern repeating or symmetrical?

How did you find these questions?  

Time to reflect

Look back through the work you have done this term. Think about what you enjoyed and what you found easy or hard. Talk about this with your teacher and someone at home.

Look back at page 8. Complete the sentences to describe the number in the place value chart. Partition it in 2 different ways.

The number in numerals is ☐

The number in words is ______________.

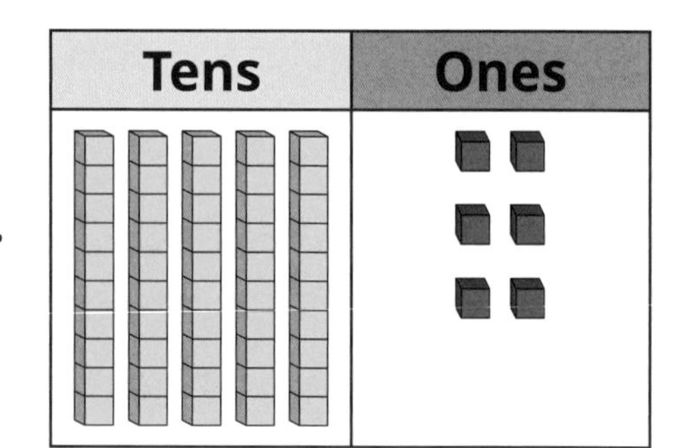

There are ☐ tens and ☐ ones.

☐ = ☐ + ☐

☐ = ☐ + ☐

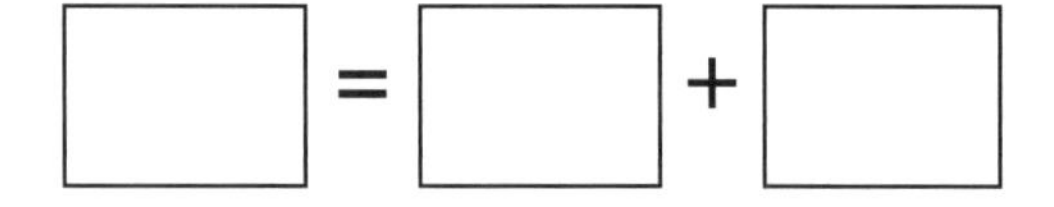

The number is 10 greater than ☐

Circle one of the statements to show how you feel about partitioning numbers.

I am confident and could teach someone else.	I think I understand but I need practice.	I don't understand and need help.

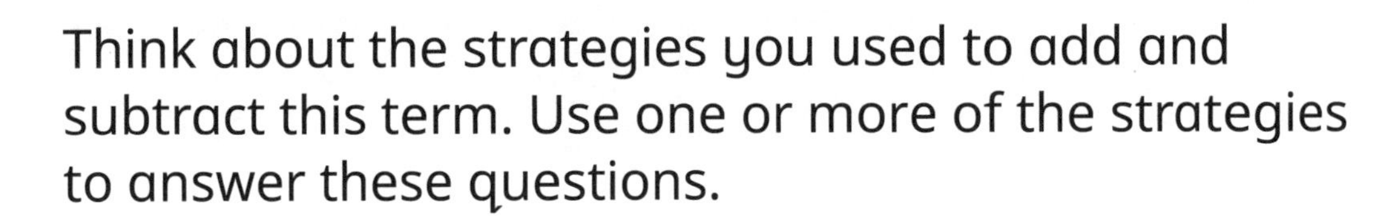
Think about the strategies you used to add and subtract this term. Use one or more of the strategies to answer these questions.

34 – 9 = ☐ 24 + 36 = ☐

56 + 7 = ☐ 64 – 23 = ☐

47 + 8 = ☐ 72 – 7 = ☐

How did you find adding and subtracting with 2-digit numbers? Circle one of the cards to show how you feel about adding and subtracting with 2-digit numbers.

1	2	3	4
I found these hard and need some help.	I need some more practice.	I can do these well and didn't make any mistakes.	I am confident and could teach someone else.

Have a think about all the work you've done this term.
What are you most confident with?
What do you still need to practise?

I feel confident with ______________________________

____.

I still need to practise ______________________________

____.

Spring term

Block 1 Money

In this block, we think about money, both **coins** and **notes**. We compare amounts of money and find **change**.

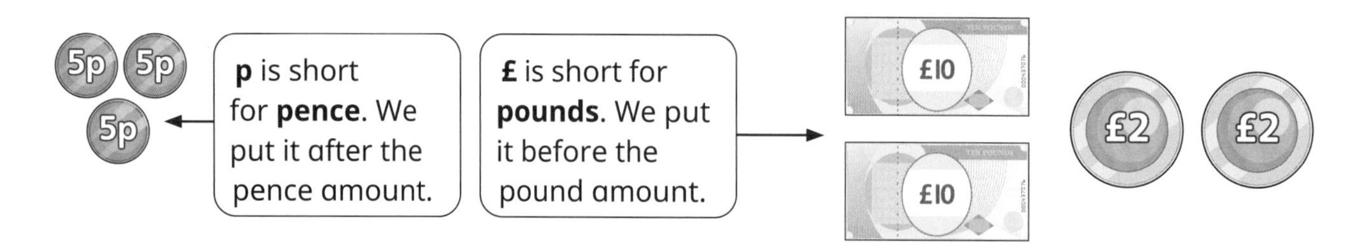

We look at pound and pence amounts together. I can see above there are two £10 notes. The **total value** is £20

There are two £2 coins. The total value is £4

There are three 5p coins. The total value is 15p

£20 + £4 + 15p = £24 and 15p

There is £24 and 15p altogether.

Change is the money you get back when you buy something with coins or notes that have a value greater than the price of the item.

I buy an apple for 46p.

I pays with a £1 coin.

How much change do I get?

We use number lines and part-whole models to help us solve change problems.

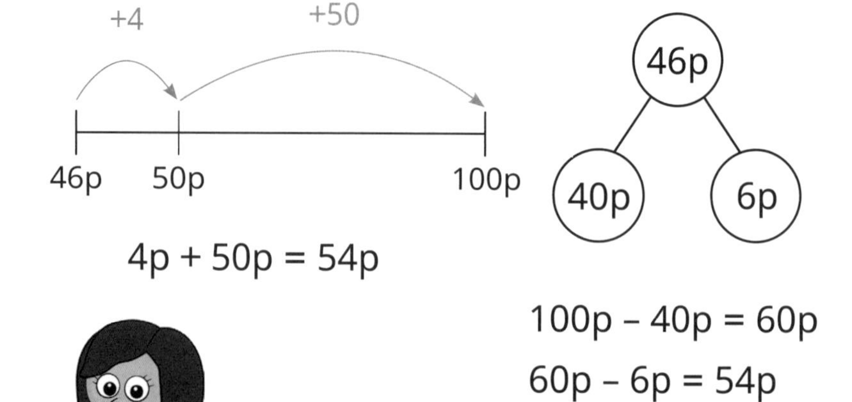

Here are some maths words that we see. What do they mean?

worth **value** **coins** **notes** **pence** **pounds** **total** **change**

Money

Date:

Let's practise

Which coins will you count first?

1 How much money is there?

a) 

☐ p

b) 

☐ p

c) 

☐ p

2 How much money is there?

a) 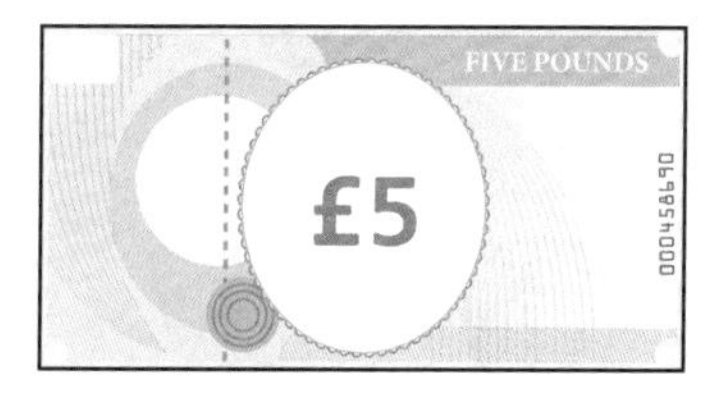

£ 

b) 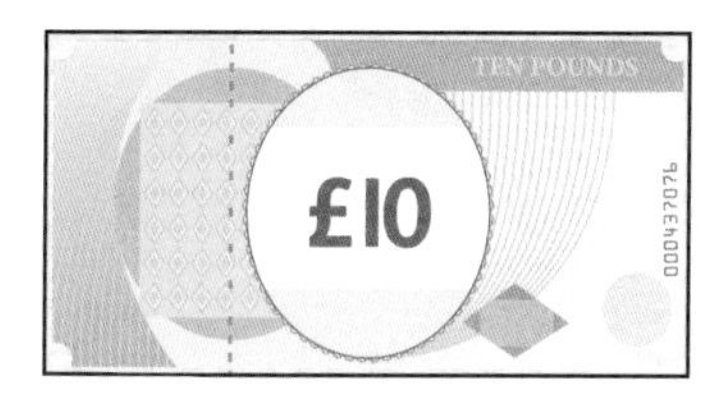

£ 

c) 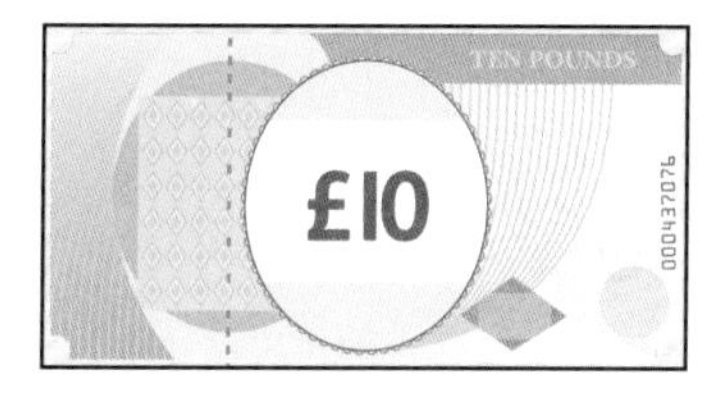

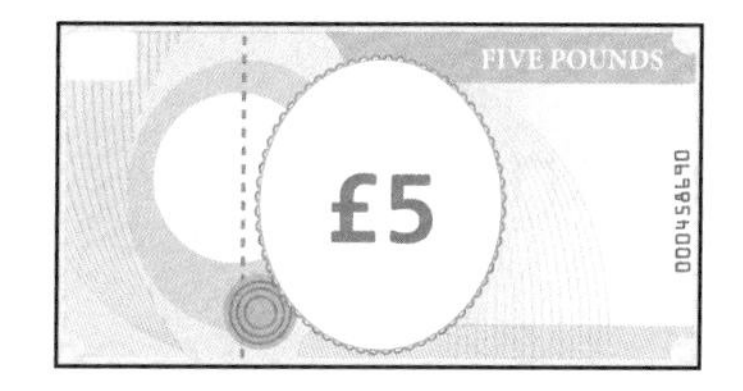

£ 

3 How much money is there?

£ ☐ and ☐ p

4 Tick £14 and 68p.

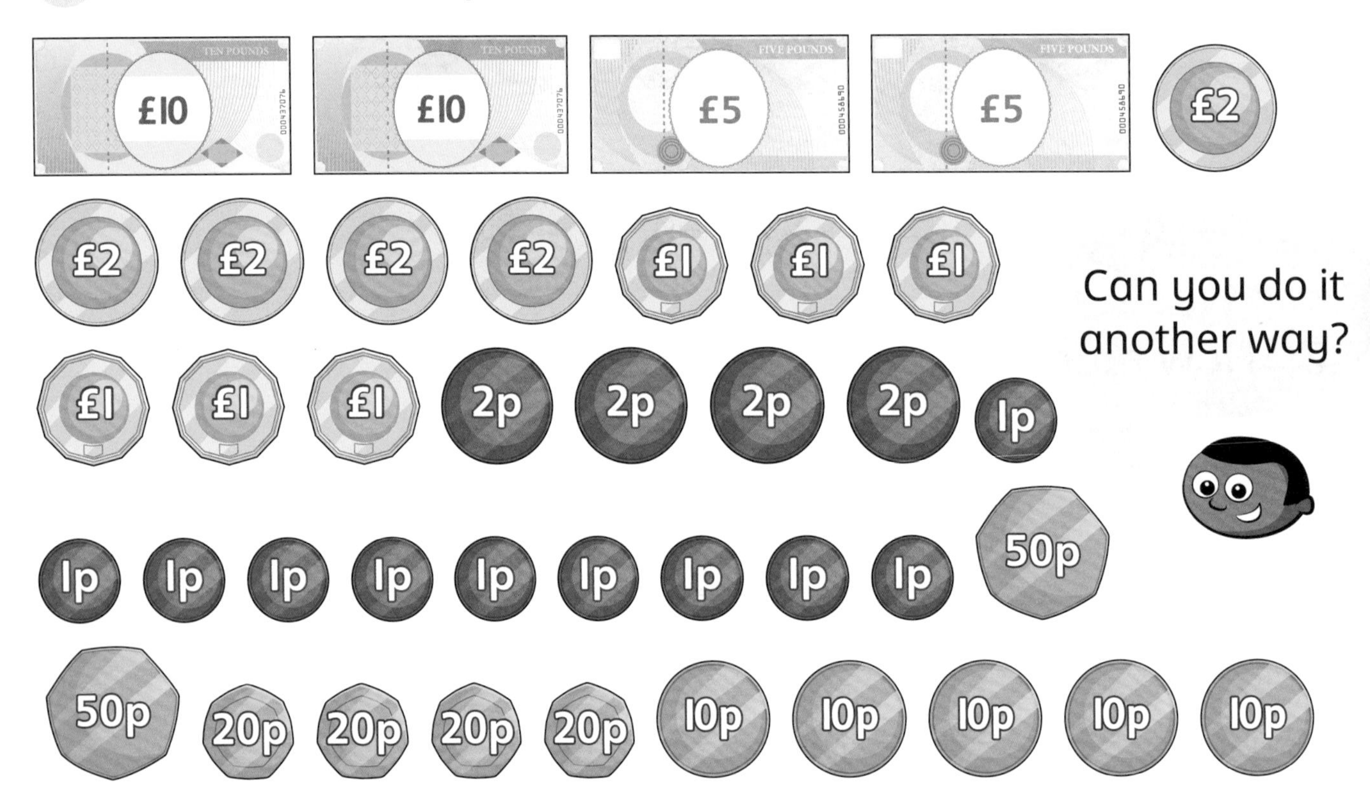

5 Ron has some money.

I have two £10 notes and 5 coins.

a) What is the greatest amount of money Ron could have? £ ☐

b) What is the least amount of money Ron could have? £ ☐ and ☐ p

Real world maths

Max has £6 and 21p.

What coins and notes could he have?

Find and draw at least 2 different possibilities.

Talk it out

Kim and Ron both have 25p, but they each have a different number of coins.

Explain to someone in your home how this is possible. Draw coins to show them.

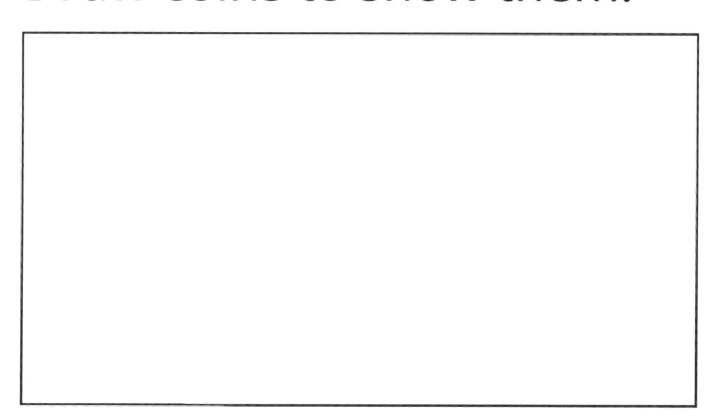

It is possible to make 25p with a different number of coins because …

How did you find these questions?   

Money

Date:

Let's practise

1 Tick the greater amount of money in each pair.

a) 

b) 

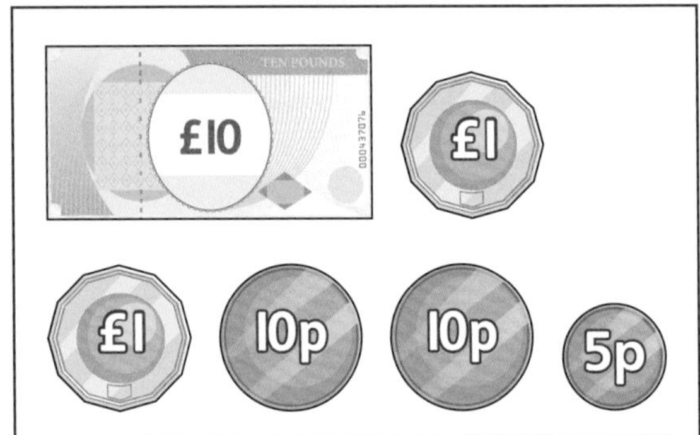

2 These items are for sale in a shop.

a) What is the total cost of a bottle of water and a magazine? £ ☐

b) What is the total cost of a football and 2 bottles of water? £ ☐

c) What is the total cost of an apple and a bag of sweets? ☐ p

3 Complete the calculations.

a) 28p + ___ p = £1

b) 56p + ___ p = £1

c) ___ p + 9p = £1

d) £1 = ___ p + 47p

4 Complete the calculations.

a) £3 and 42p + £6 and 9p = £ ___ and ___ p

b) £7 and 28p – £2 and 10p = £ ___ and ___ p

c) £5 and 27p + £13 and 43p = £ ___ and ___ p

5 A hat costs £12 and 95p.

A scarf costs £8 and 45p.

a) How much more does the hat cost than the scarf?

£ ___ and ___ p

b) What is the total cost of the hat and the scarf?

£ ___ and ___ p

6 A pen costs 26p.

When you pay more than needed, the money you get back is the **change**.

A pencil costs 17p.

Jack buys 2 pens and 2 pencils.

He pays with a £1 coin.

How much change does he get?  p

Real world maths

Make £1 in 4 different ways.

Draw your answers.

How many pence are there in one pound?

Think it out

Mo has £18 and 42p.

Jo has £23 and 57p.

Max has more money than Mo, but less money than Jo.

How much money could Max have? ______________________

Draw the notes and coins Max could have.

How did you find these questions?   

Block 2 Multiplication and division

In this block, we explore multiplication, starting by thinking about **equal groups**.

There are 4 equal groups of apples.
There are 2 in each group.
There are 4 groups of 2
4 **lots** of 2

$2 + 2 + 2 + 2 = 8$

4 **times** 2 equals 8

$4 \times 2 = 8$

There are 8 altogether.

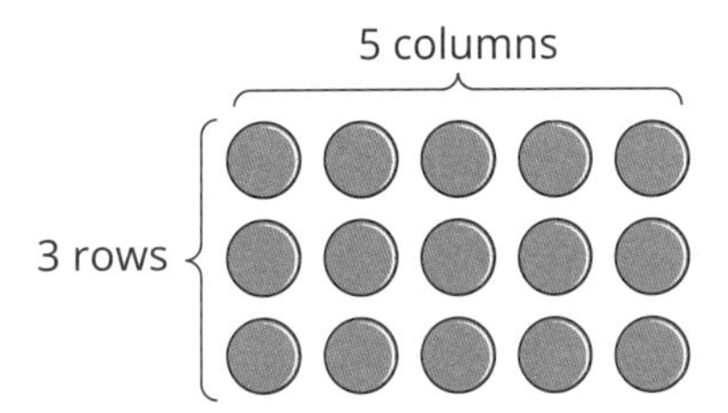

We also use **arrays** to show multiplication.

There are 3 **rows** and 5 **columns**.

$3 \times 5 = 15$ and $5 \times 3 = 15$

We also **divide**. One way we can think of division is putting things into groups of a certain amount.
These 12 pencils have been put into groups of 2
There are 6 groups.

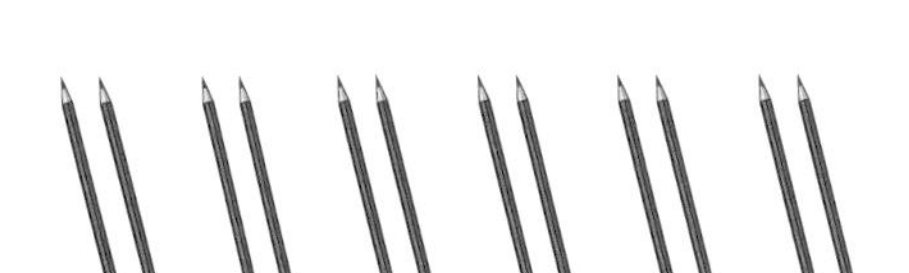

12 divided by 2 equals 6
$12 \div 2 = 6$

Another way we can think of division is **sharing** things between a certain number of groups.
These 12 pencils have been shared into 3 groups.
There are 4 pencils in each group.

12 divided by 3 equals 4

$12 \div 3 = 4$

Here are some maths words that we see. What do they mean?

multiply array lots groups of divide sharing grouping
odd even halving doubling times times-table

Multiplication and division

Date:

Let's practise

1 Are the groups equal or unequal?

Circle your answers.

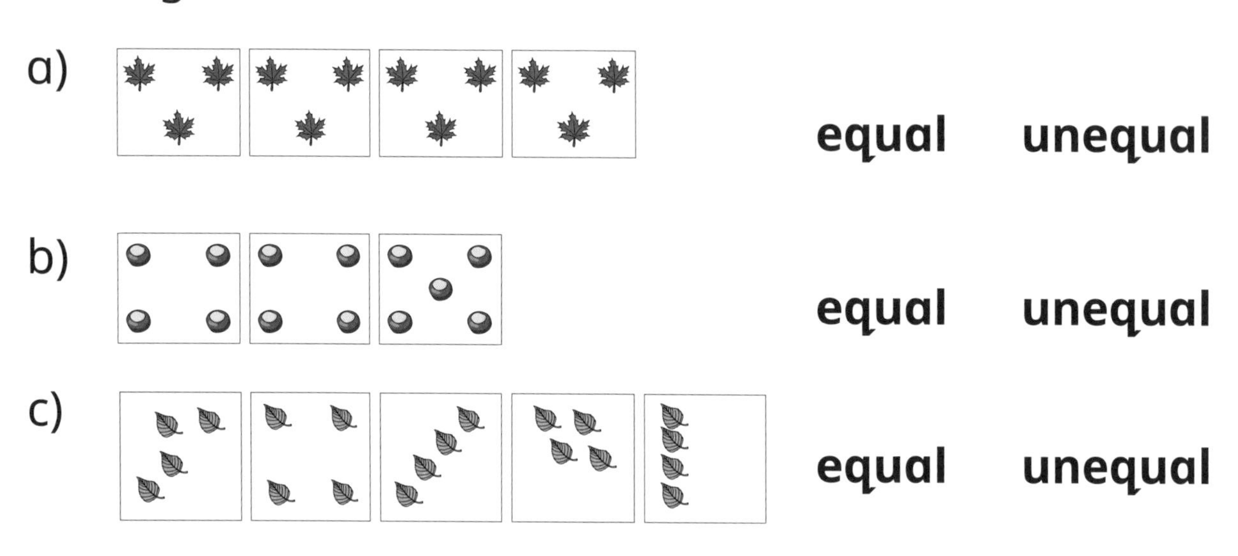

a) **equal** **unequal**

b) **equal** **unequal**

c) **equal** **unequal**

2 Complete the sentences to describe the groups.

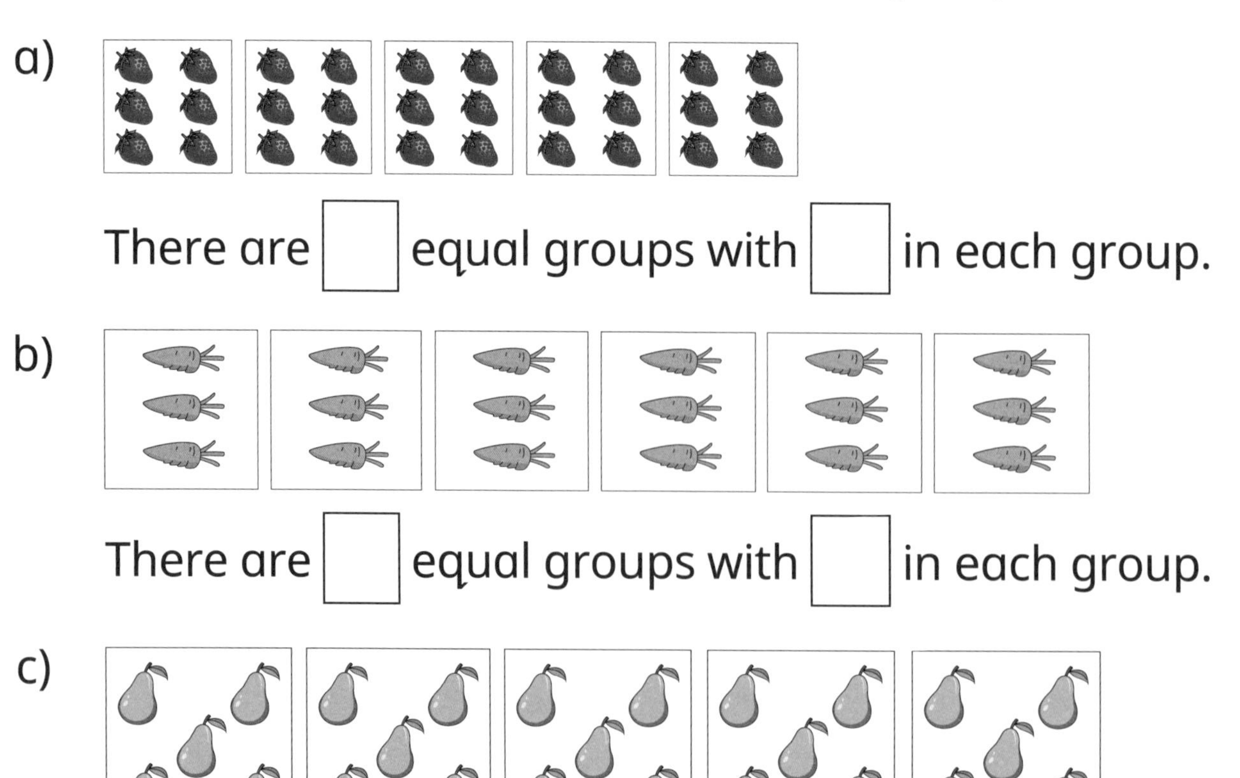

a) There are ☐ equal groups with ☐ in each group.

b) There are ☐ equal groups with ☐ in each group.

c) There are ☐ equal groups with ☐ in each group.

3 How many are there altogether?

Complete the sentences.

a)

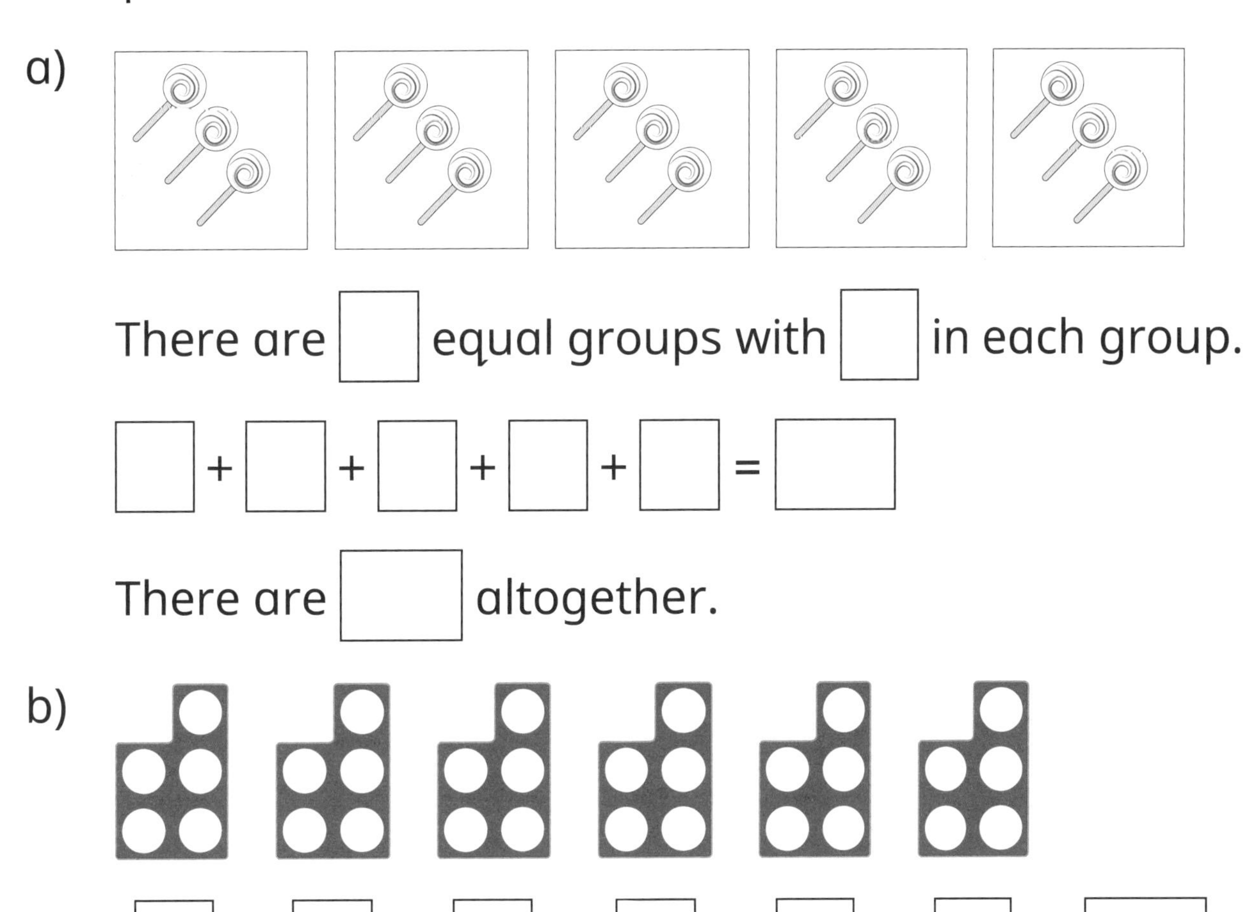

There are ☐ equal groups with ☐ in each group.

☐ + ☐ + ☐ + ☐ + ☐ = ☐

There are ☐ altogether.

b)

☐ + ☐ + ☐ + ☐ + ☐ + ☐ = ☐

4 Tiny has tried to arrange the cakes into equal groups.

a) Explain why Tiny's groups aren't equal.

____

b) How can Tiny move 1 cake to make the groups equal?

____

Real world maths

Find some small objects around your home, like buttons or pieces of pasta.

Arrange your objects into equal groups.
Set aside any objects left over.

Complete the sentences to describe your groups.

There are ☐ equal groups with ☐ in each group.

There are ☐ altogether.

How many different ways can you arrange your objects into equal groups?

How did you find these questions?  

Multiplication and division

Date:

Let's practise

1 Complete the sentences to match the pictures.

a)     

There are ☐ equal groups with ☐ in each group.

☐ + ☐ + ☐ + ☐ + ☐ = ☐

☐ × ☐ = ☐

There are ☐ altogether.

b) 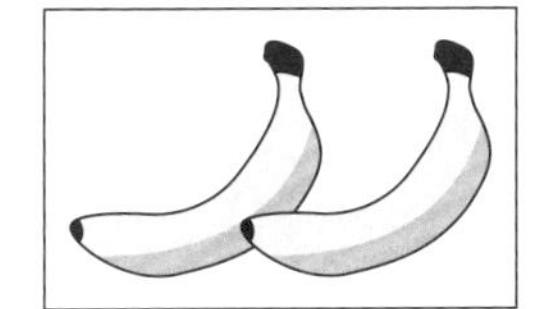  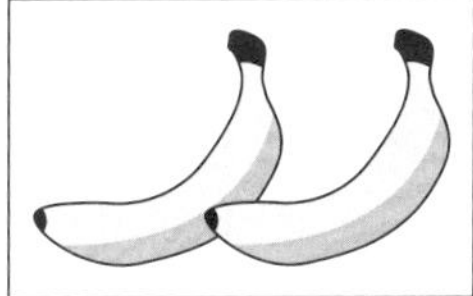 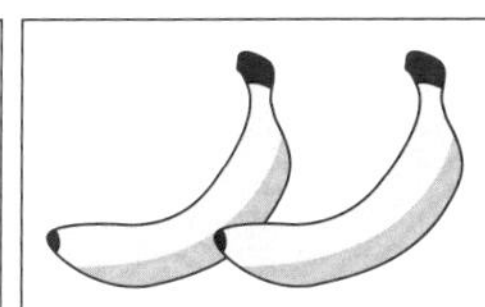

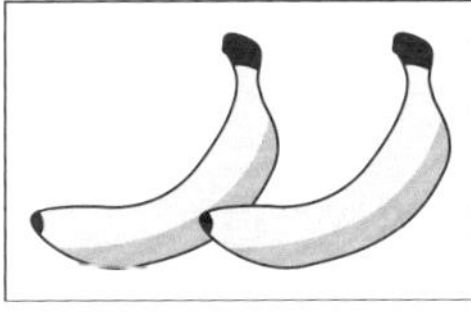 

There are ☐ equal groups with ☐ in each group.

☐ + ☐ + ☐ + ☐ + ☐ + ☐ + ☐ = ☐

☐ × ☐ = ☐

There are ☐ altogether.

2 Write 2 additions and 2 multiplications that this array shows.

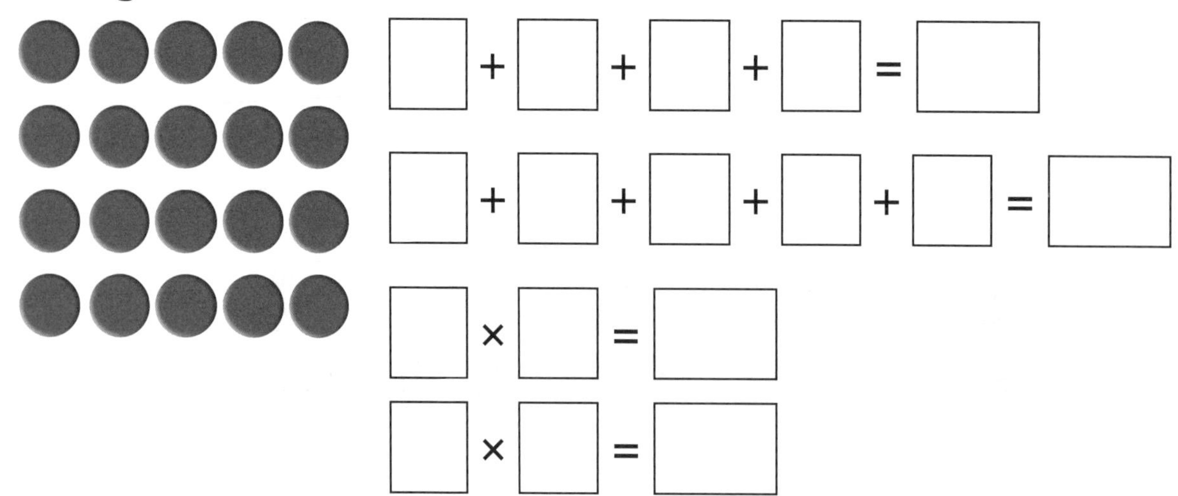

3 Complete the table.

Addition	Multiplication
3 + 3 + 3 + 3	□ × 3
	2 × 5
4 + 4	
7 + 7 + 7 + 7 + 7	
	6 × 10

4 Sam has made an array using counters.

One of the multiplications that describes my array is 4 × 10 = 40

Write 1 more multiplication and 2 additions to describe Sam's array.

___

___

___

Real world maths

Use an even number of pieces of pasta, or another set of small objects, to make an array.

Draw your array.

Remember, an **array** is a way of arranging things in rows and columns.

Describe your array using addition and multiplication.

______________________ ______________________

______________________ ______________________

Think it out

Jack makes an array using counters.

It has twice as many rows as columns.

He uses 18 counters in total.

Draw Jack's array.

How many rows and columns are there?

How did you find these questions?   

Multiplication and division

Date:

Let's practise

1 Ron and Max each have this many apples.

a) Ron puts the apples on plates with 4 apples on each plate.

Draw a picture to show how Ron groups the apples and complete the sentences.

There are ☐ apples.

There are 4 apples on each plate.

There are ☐ plates.

☐ ÷ 4 = ☐

b) Max shares his apples equally between 4 boxes.

Draw to show how Max shares the apples and complete the sentences.

There are ☐ apples.

There are 4 boxes.

There are ☐ apples in each box.

☐ ÷ 4 = ☐

2 Write a 2 times-table fact to match each picture.

a) 

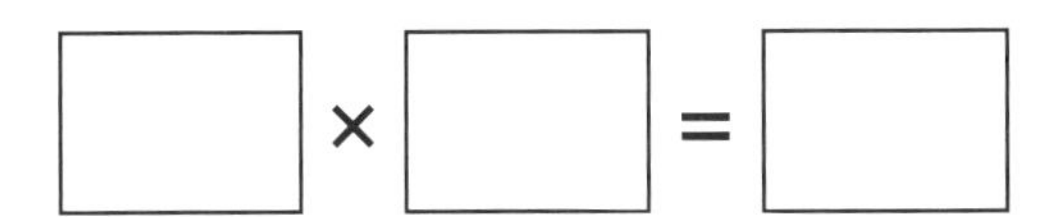

b) 

☐ × ☐ = ☐

c) 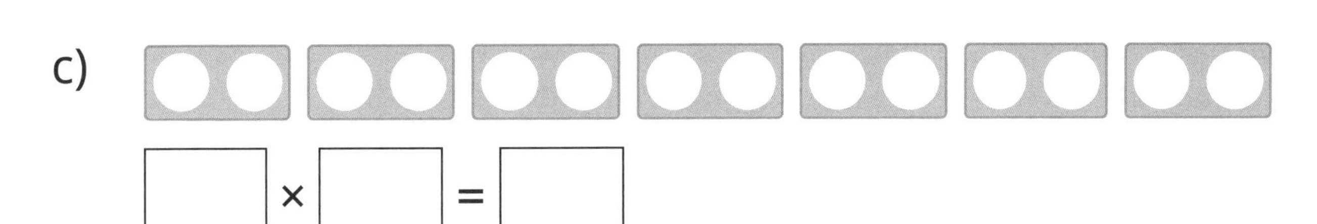

☐ × ☐ = ☐

3 Complete the calculations.

a) $8 \times 2 =$ ☐

b) $2 \times 4 =$ ☐

c) $10 \times 2 =$ ☐

d) $20 \div 2 =$ ☐

e) $4 \div 2 =$ ☐

f) ☐ $= 22 \div 2$

4 Ron has £5

Max has twice as much money as Ron.

Jack has twice as much money as Max.

How much money do they have altogether? £ ☐

How can the
2 times-table help you?

Real world maths

Find 32 small objects around your home, such as pieces of pasta or buttons.

Share the objects into 8 equal groups.

How many objects are in each group? ☐

Group the objects into groups of 8

How many groups are there? ☐

What do you notice?

Think it out

Sam is thinking about multiplication.

I know 7×2 is equal to 5×2 add 2×2

Is Sam correct? ______________

Draw an array to help you explain how you know.

Write three ways that you could work out 9×2

☐ × ☐ add ☐ × ☐

☐ × ☐ add ☐ × ☐

☐ × ☐ add ☐ × ☐

How did you find these questions?   

Multiplication and division

Date:

Let's practise

1 Draw counters to show doubles.

When you **double** a number, you multiply by 2

a) 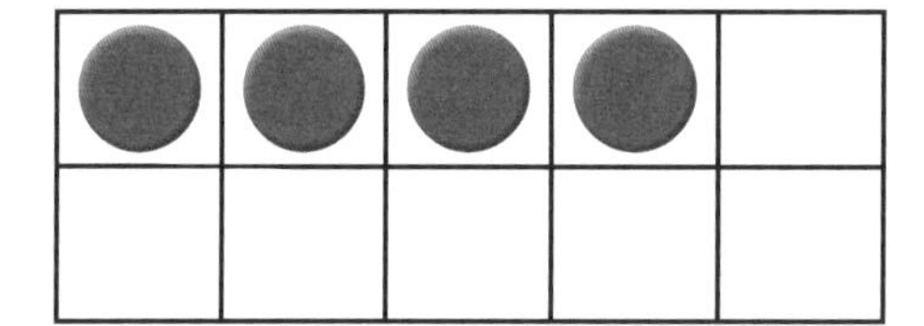

Double 4 is ☐

b) 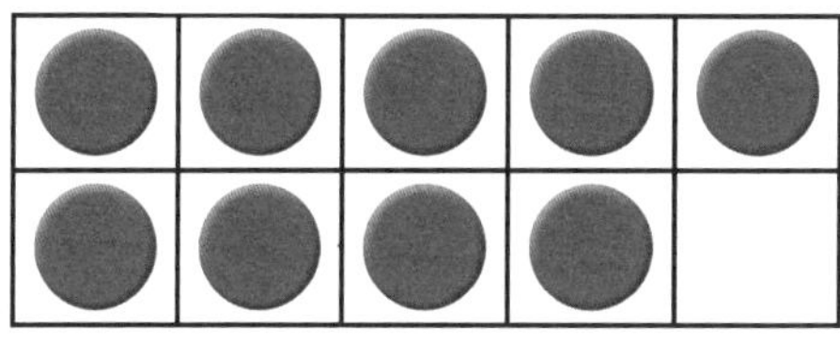 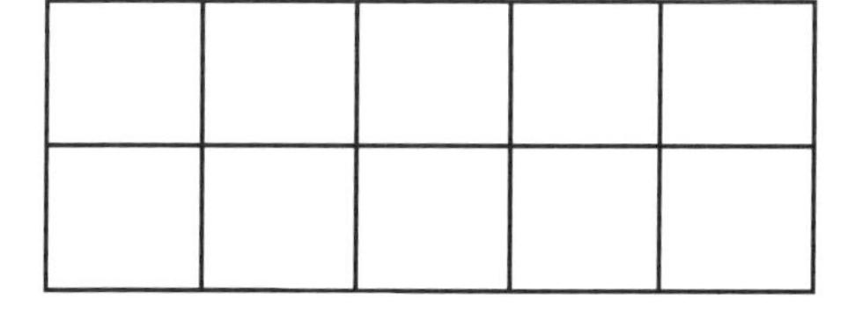

Double 9 is ☐

c) 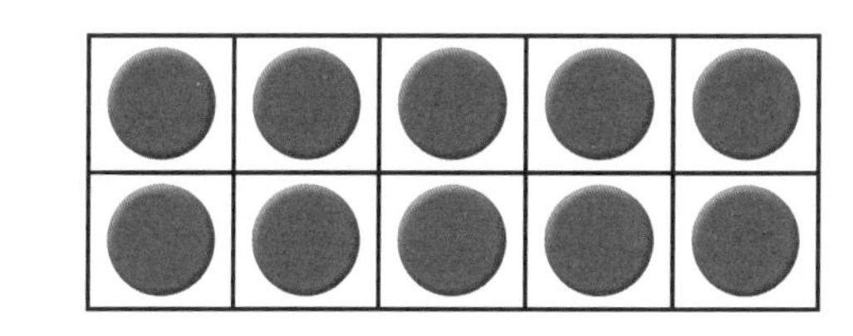 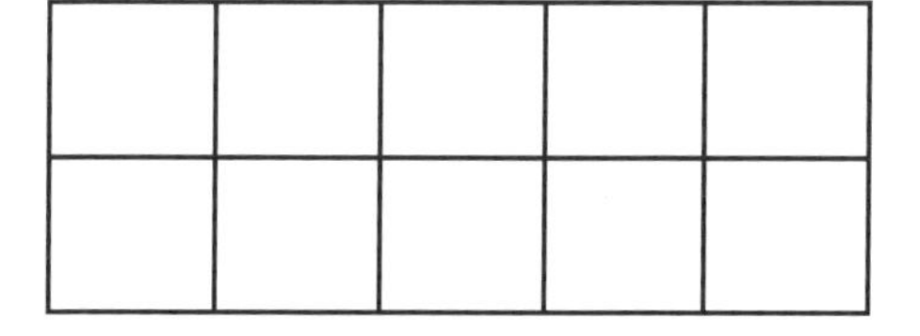

Double 10 is ☐

2 Complete the sentences.

a) Double 6 is equal to ☐ + ☐

Double 6 is equal to 2 × ☐

Double 6 is equal to ☐

b) Double 12 is equal to ☐ + ☐

Double 12 is equal to 2 × ☐

Double 12 is equal to ☐

3 Circle the even numbers.

11 6 3 9 12 30 83 72 64 29

How do you know? ____

____

4 What is half of each number?

a) 16 $\square$

b) 24 $\square$

c) 18 $\square$

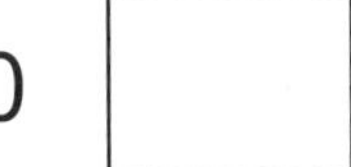

d) 40 $\square$

5 Use the base 10 to complete the multiplications.

a) 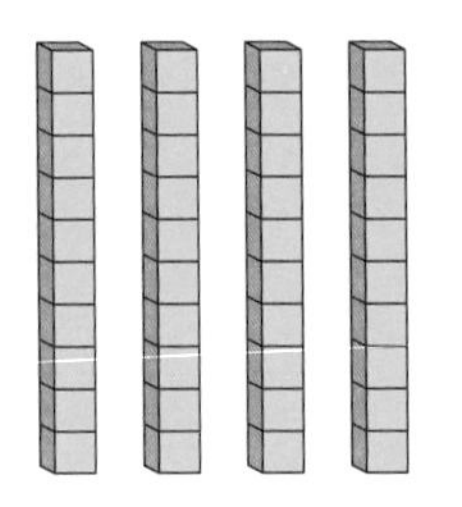

$4 \times 10 = \square$

b) 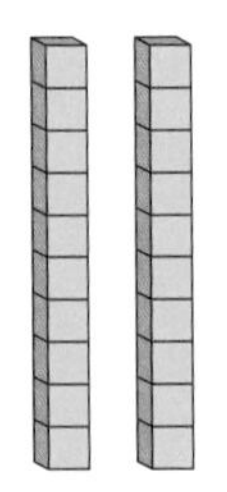

$2 \times 10 = \square$

c) 

$10 \times 7 = \square$

d) 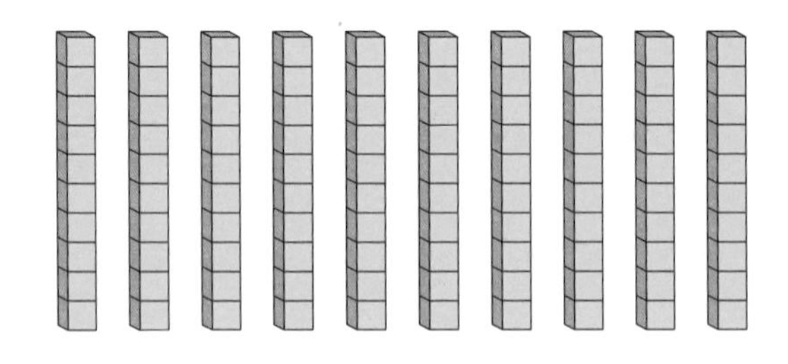

$\square = 10 \times 10$

6 Complete the divisions.

a) $70 \div 10 = \square$

b) $30 \div 10 = \square$

c) $\square = 80 \div 10$

d) $10 \div \square = 1$

How many groups of 10 can you make?

Think it out

Double ◣ = 18 Half of ● = 2

Work out ◣ × 10 ☐

Work out ● × 10 ☐

Find the difference between the two new numbers. ☐

Tell someone how you worked it out.

Talk it out

What does it mean to double a number?

What does it mean to halve a number?

If you double a number then halve it, what do you notice?

Share your answers with someone in your home.

Double … is …
Half of … is …

If I know what double …
is, I can find half of …

How did you find these questions?   

Multiplication and division

Date:

Let's practise

1 Use the pictures to complete the multiplications.

a) $6 \times 5 =$ ☐

b) $7 \times 5 =$ ☐

c) $8 \times 5\text{p} =$ ☐ p

d) $£5 \times 3 = £$ ☐

e) $5 \times 4 =$ ☐

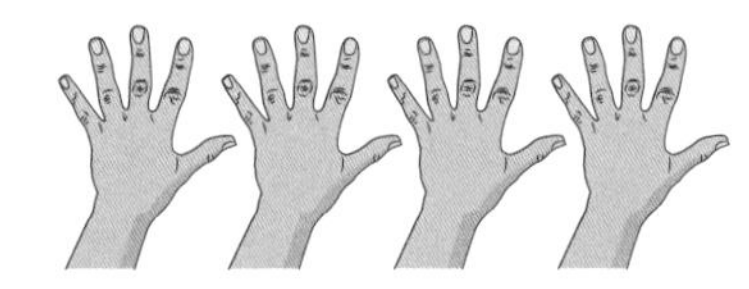

2 Complete the calculations.

a) $3 \times 5 =$ ☐

b) ☐ $= 1 \times 5$

c) $7 \times 5 =$ ☐

d) $20 \div 5 =$ ☐

e) ☐ $= 40 \div 5$

f) $50 \div 5 =$ ☐

How could drawing an array help you?

3 Complete the number tracks.

0	5	10								

0	10	20								

What do you notice?

4 Here is a number line.

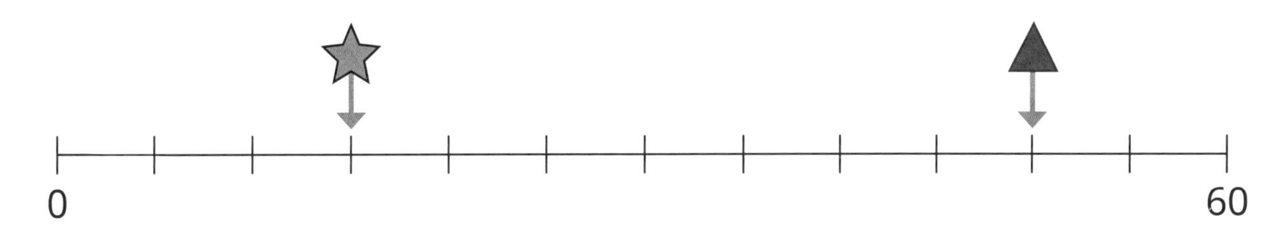

Work out ▲ − ★ = ☐

Does the number line go up in 5s or 10s?

5 Tiny is thinking about multiplication.

The 5 times-table is double the 10 times-table.

Do you agree with Tiny? ________

Explain your answer.

____

____

6 How many 5p coins do you need to make £1?

Think it out

Max, Jo and Sam are working out 18 × 5

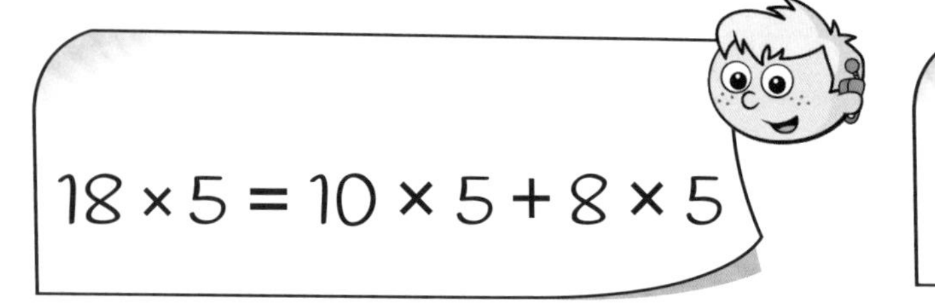

18 × 5 = 20 × 5 − 2 × 5

18 × 5 = 9 × 2 × 5

Work out 18 × 5 using each method.

[ ]

Work out 17 × 5 = [ ]

Which method did you use? Why?

How did you find these questions?   

Spring term

Block 3 Length and height

In this block, we measure how **long** and how **tall** things are using standard units of measure.

You can use a **ruler** to measure. This ruler is 15 **centimetres** long. The length of this line is 11 cm.

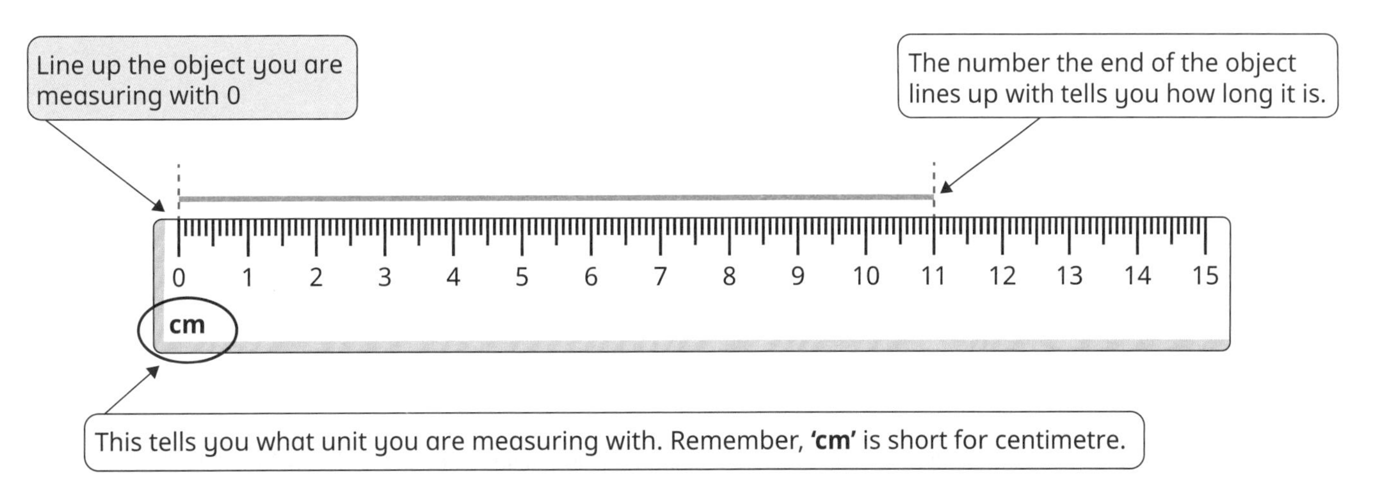

You can also measure items in **metres** using a **metre stick**. A metre is **longer** than a centimetre.

Remember, **m** is short for metre. Always remember to record your units with your answers.

We can compare and order **lengths** and **heights**. You can use the symbols **<**, **=** and **>**.

5 cm > 3 cm — 5 centimetres is longer than 3 centimetres.

10 cm < 10 m — 10 centimetres is **shorter** than 10 metres.

Here are some maths words that we see. What do they mean?

centimetre **metre** **ruler** **metre stick** **length** **height**
longer **longest** **shorter** **shortest** **taller** **tallest**

Length and height

Date:

Let's practise

1 What is the length of each line?

a)

0 1 2 3 4 5 6 7 8 9 10 11 12 13 14 15
cm

☐ cm

b)

0 1 2 3 4 5 6 7 8 9 10 11 12 13 14 15
cm

☐ cm

c)

0 1 2 3 4 5 6 7 8 9 10 11 12 13 14 15
cm

☐ cm

2 Use a ruler to draw the lines.

Where on the ruler do you need to start measuring from?

a) 5 cm long

b) 9 cm long

c) 10 cm long

3 How long is each object?

a)

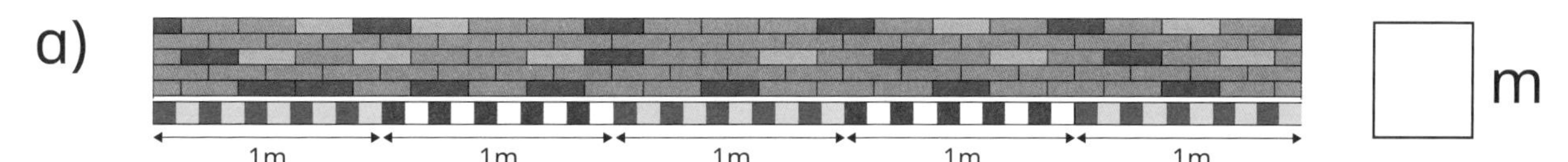

☐ m

b)

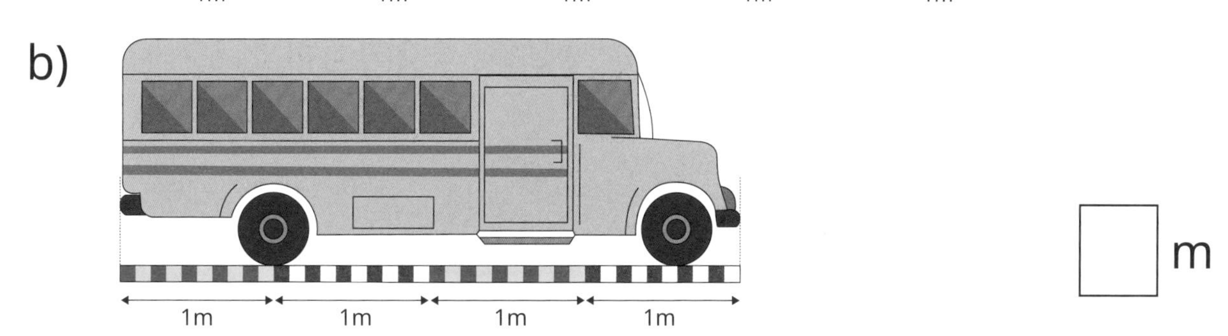

☐ m

4 Tiny is measuring the length of the pencil.

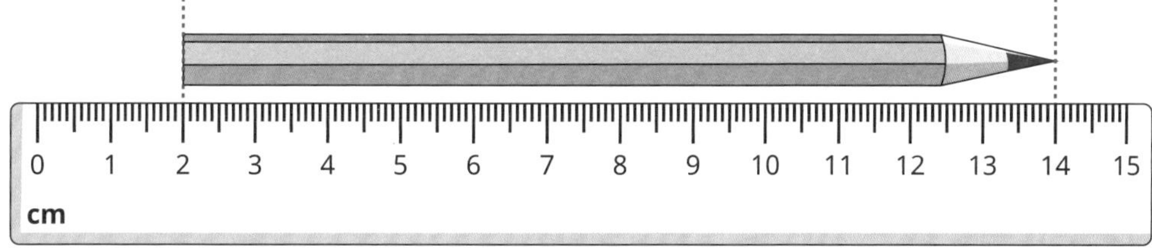

The pencil is 14 cm long.

a) Explain Tiny's mistake.

____

b) How long is the pencil? ☐ cm

5 Here are 3 lines.

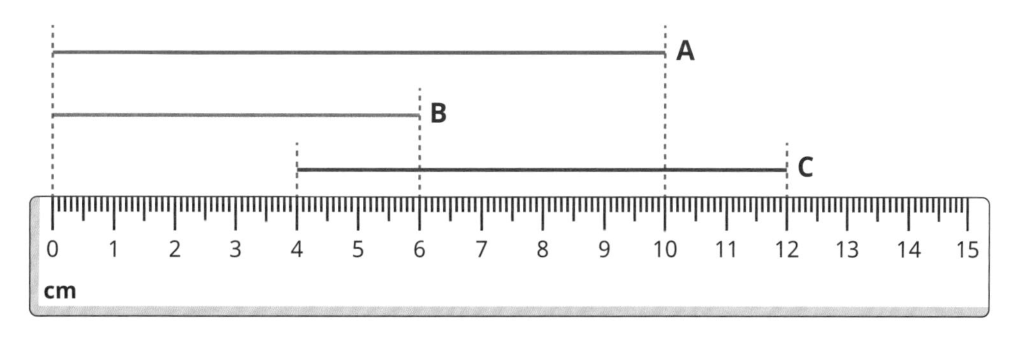

a) How long is each line?

A = ☐ cm B = ☐ cm C = ☐ cm

b) Which line is the longest? ☐

c) Which line is the shortest? ☐

Real world maths

Use a ruler to measure the length of different objects in your home.

Record them in the table.

I am going to compare the lengths of my objects!

Object	Length

Think it out

A polar bear is 2 m tall.

A giraffe is 5 m tall.

An elephant is taller than a polar bear, but shorter than a giraffe.

How many metres tall could the elephant be? ☐ m

Is there more than one possible answer?

How did you find these questions?   

Length and height

Date:

Let's practise

1 Here are some pieces of ribbon.

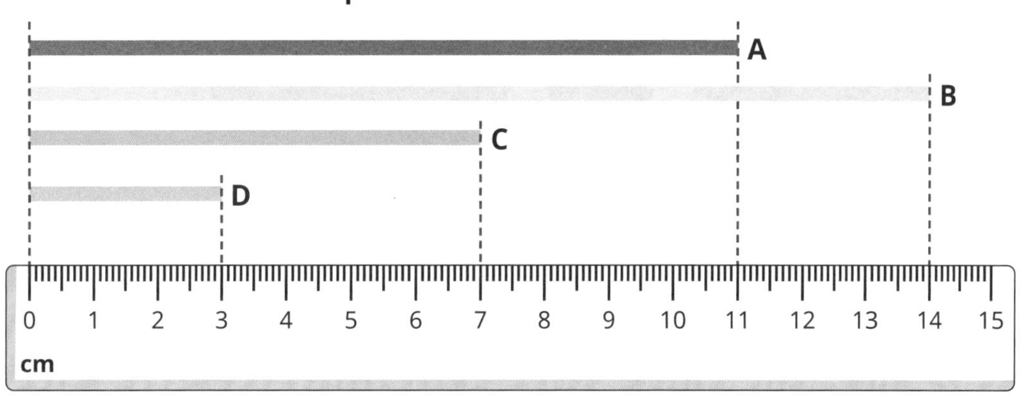

Order the ribbons from shortest to longest.

☐ ☐ ☐ ☐

shortest longest

2 Here are some pencils.

Which pencil is the longest? How do you know?

A
B
C
D
0 1 2 3 4 5 6 7 8 9 10 11 12 13 14 15
cm

Order the pencils from longest to shortest.

☐ ☐ ☐ ☐

longest shortest

3 Here are some bears.

Order the bears from tallest to shortest.

☐ ☐ ☐

tallest shortest

4 Complete the calculations.

a) 8 cm + 5 cm = ☐ cm

b) 15 m – 7 m = ☐ m

c) 24 cm + 42 cm = ☐ cm

d) 63 m – 51 m = ☐ m

5 A house is 5 m tall.

A shop is twice as tall as the house.

How tall is the shop? ☐ m

6 Amir is 84 cm tall.

Jack is 6 cm shorter than Amir.

Ron is 15 cm taller than Jack.

How tall is Ron? ☐ cm

What do you need to do first? How do you know?

Think it out

A football pitch is 100 m long.

The width of the football pitch is half the length.

How wide is the football pitch?

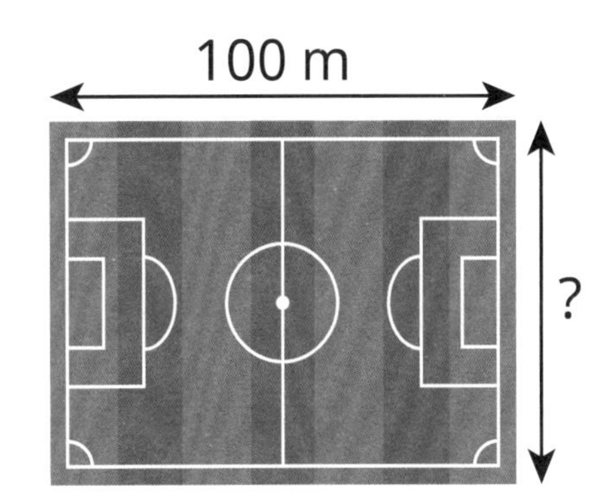

 m

A netball court is 15 m wide.

The length of the netball court is double its width.
How long is the netball court?

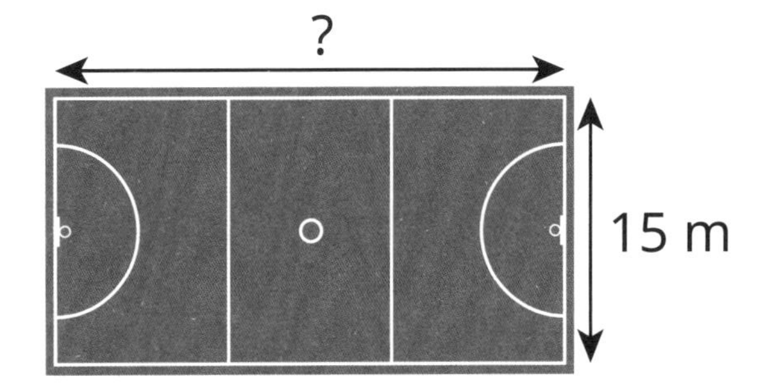

 m

How did you find these questions?  

Block 4 Mass, capacity and temperature

In this block, we measure **mass**, **volume** or **capacity**, and **temperature**. We use different units of measure for each.

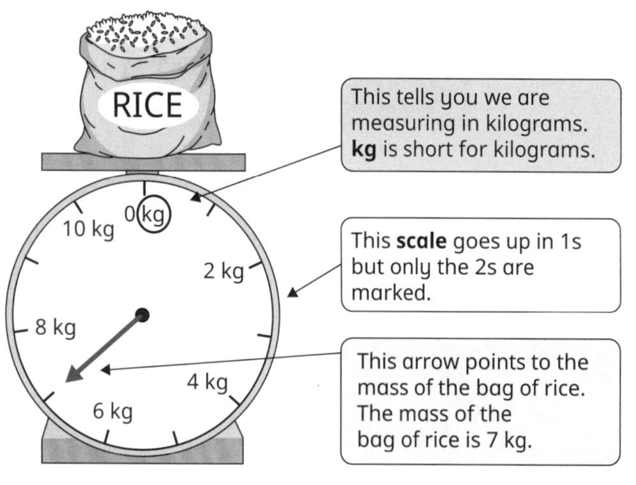

We will use **kilograms** and **grams** to work out the **mass** of objects. When we talk about mass we are talking about how heavy something is.

We use **litres** and **millilitres** to measure and describe the capacity of containers and volume of liquids.

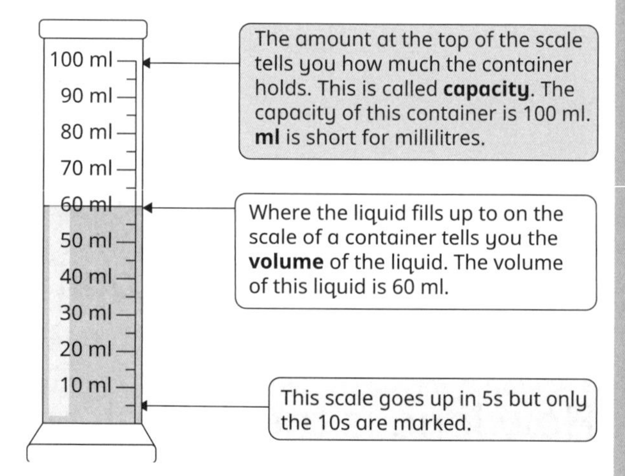

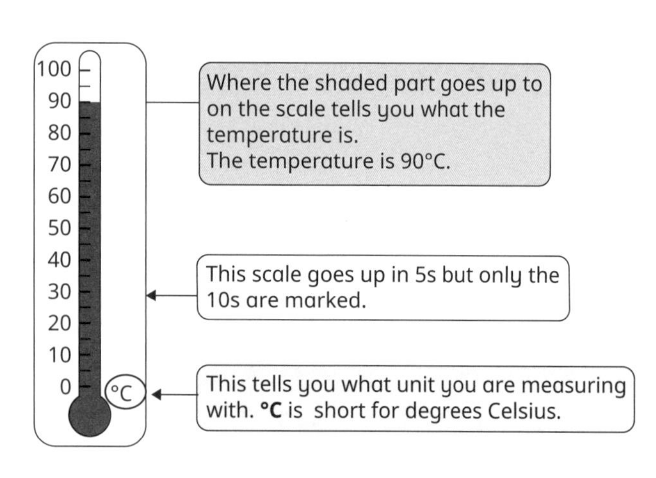

We measure temperature in **degrees Celsius**.
A thermometer measures and displays the temperature.

Here are some maths words that we see. What do they mean?

mass **volume** **kilogram** **gram** **capacity** **litre**
millilitre **temperature** **degrees Celsius**

Mass, capacity and temperature

Date:

Let's practise

1 Which object is heavier? Circle your answer.

a) 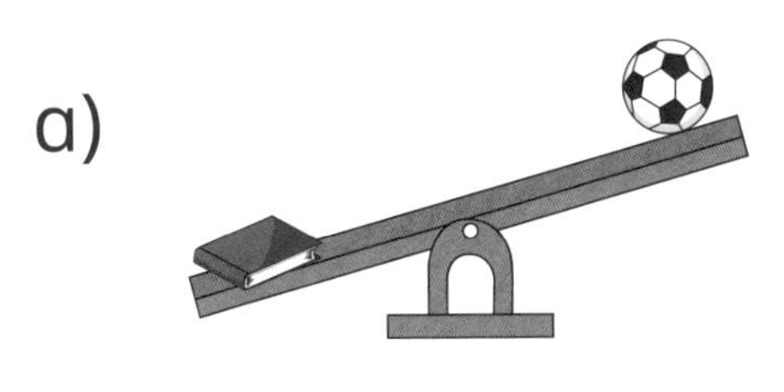

b) 

Objects with more mass are **heavier**. Objects with less mass are **lighter**.

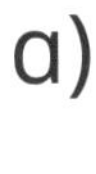

2 Which object is lighter? Circle your answer.

a) 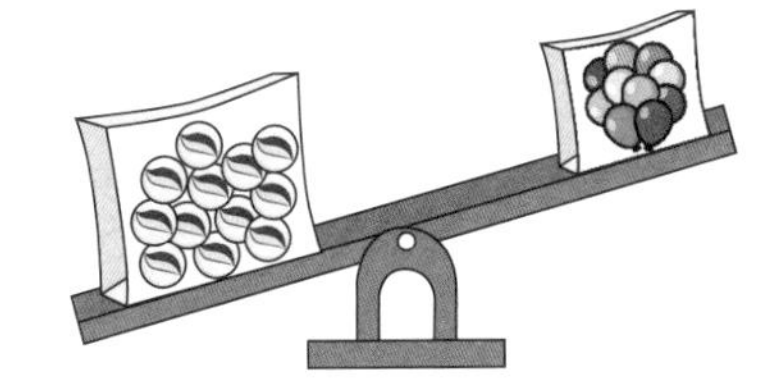

b) 

3 Which is heavier, the cylinder or the sphere?

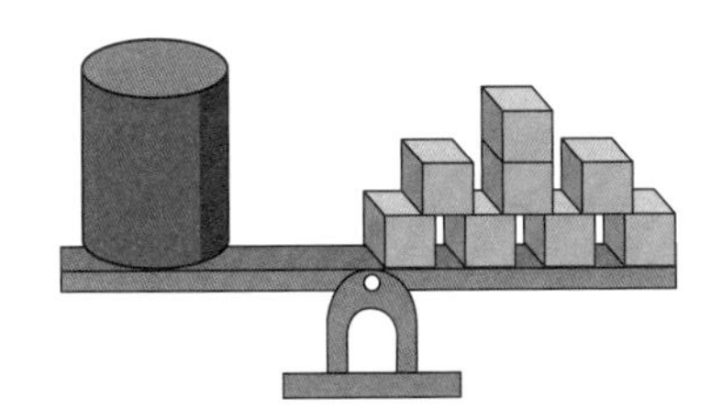

The ______________ is heavier.

How do you know?

____

____

4 What is the mass of each object?

a) [ ] g

c) [ ] kg

b) [ ] kg

d) [ ] kg

5 Here are three boxes.

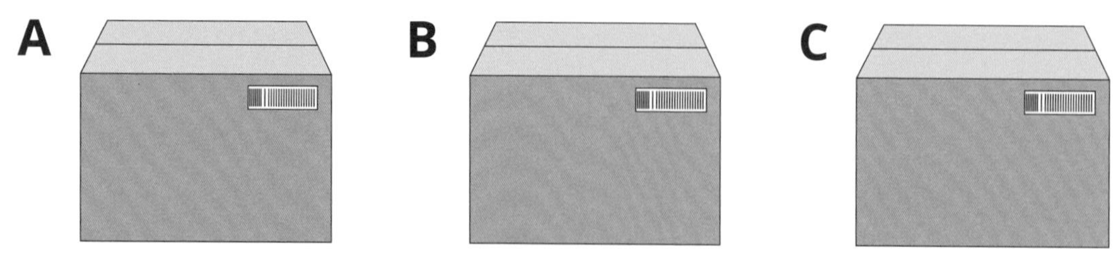

The mass of box A is 30 kg.

The mass of box B is half the mass of box A.

The total mass of boxes B and C is 32 kg.

What is the mass of box C? [ ] kg

Real world maths

Use a balance scale to compare the mass of different objects around your home.

If you don't have a balance scale, hold an object in each hand.

Write the names of the objects below.

Say which is lighter or heavier.

Decide which object you think is heavier or lighter.

The ________________ is heavier than the ________________

The ________________ is lighter than the ________________

Can you find any objects that have the same mass?

Think it out

Both objects have a mass of 12 cubes so they must have the same mass.

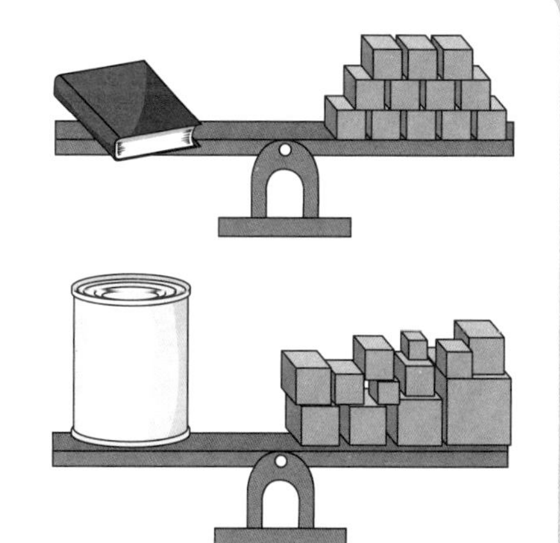

Explain why Tiny is wrong.

____

____

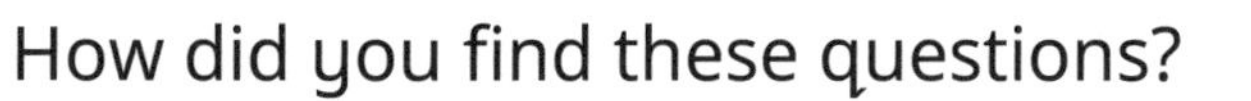

How did you find these questions?

Mass, capacity and temperature

Date:

Let's practise

1 Ron is using weights to find the mass of different objects.

a) What is the mass of the yo-yo? ☐ g

b) What is the mass of the scissors? ☐ g

c) How much lighter are the scissors than the yo-yo?
☐ g

d) What is the total mass of the scissors and the yo-yo? ☐ g

2 The scales show the mass of 2 pieces of fruit.

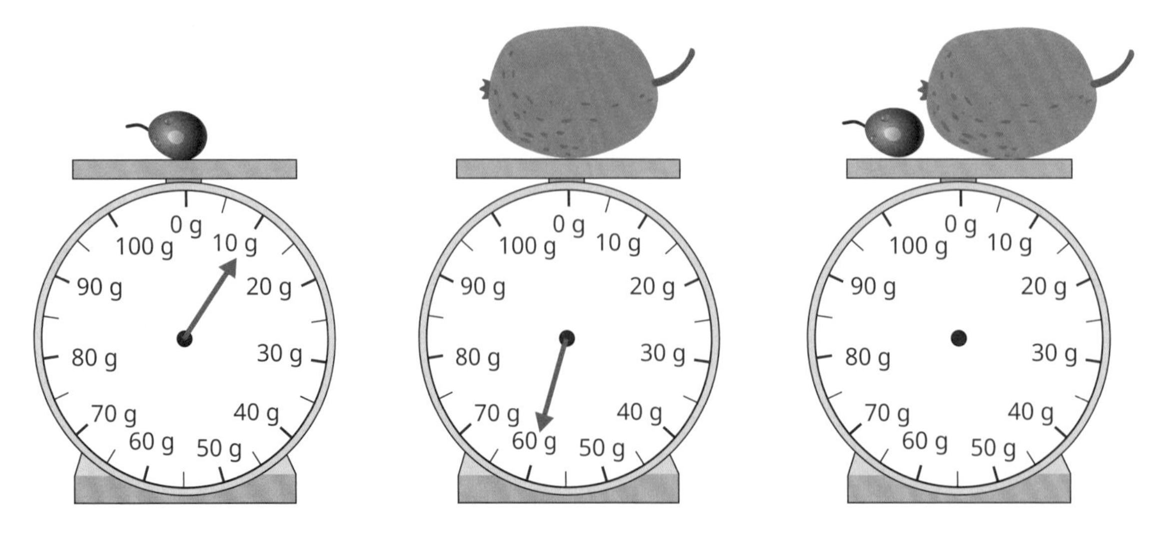

Draw an arrow on the last scale to show the total mass of the 2 pieces of fruit.

3 Which container has the greater capacity?
Circle your answer.

Capacity is the amount a container can hold. **Volume** is the amount of space an object takes up.

4 What is the volume of the liquid in each jug?

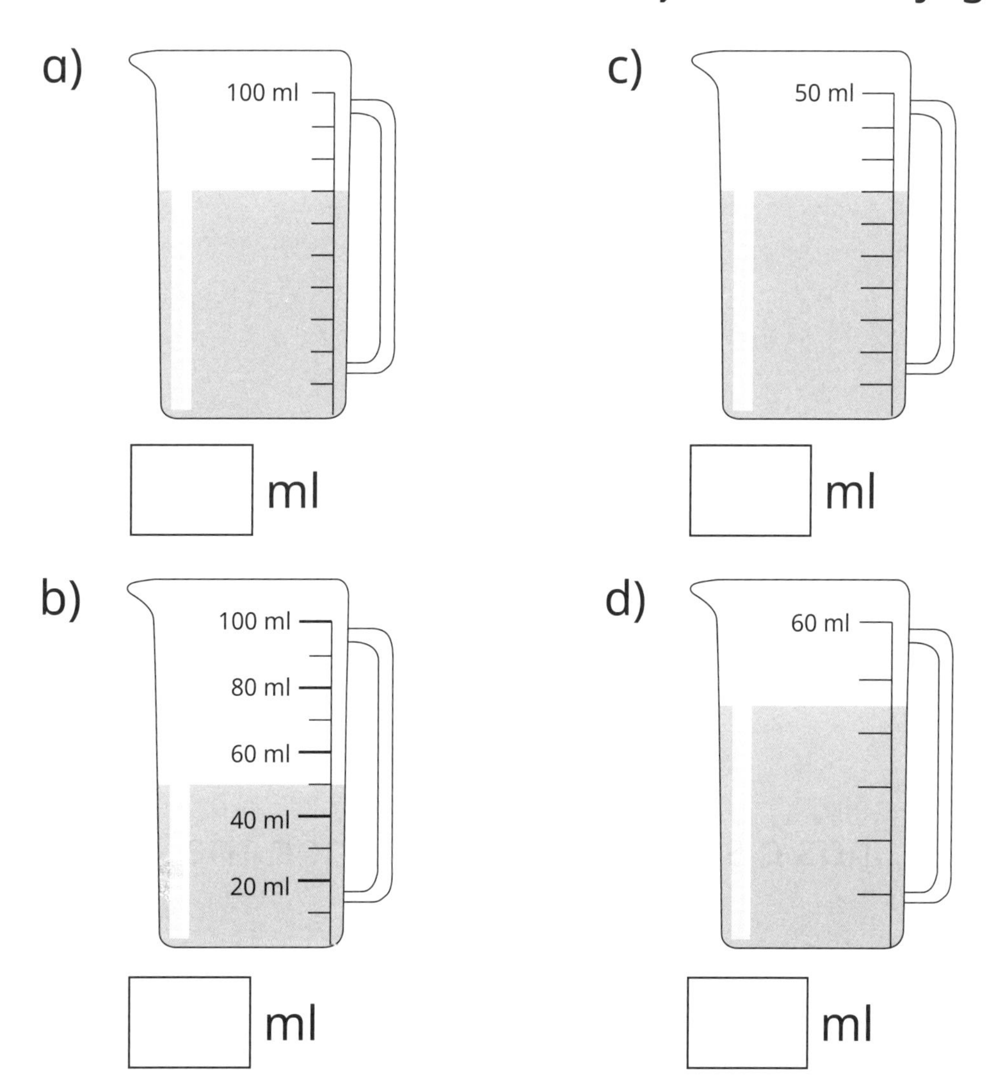

5 The mass of an empty box is 1 kg.
The mass of a bag of pasta is 2 kg.
12 bags of pasta are put in a box.
What is the total mass of the box and the pasta?

☐ kg

Real world maths

Find containers around your home with different capacities.

Ask an adult to help you.

How can you check the capacity of different containers?

Which container has the greatest capacity? ______________

Which has the smallest capacity? ______________

The ____________ has a greater capacity than the

____________.

The ____________ has a smaller capacity than the

____________.

Which objects can you compare just by looking at them?

____

____

Which do you need to check? ______________

How did you find these questions?   

Mass, capacity and temperature

Date:

Let's practise

1 What is the volume of the liquid in each jug?

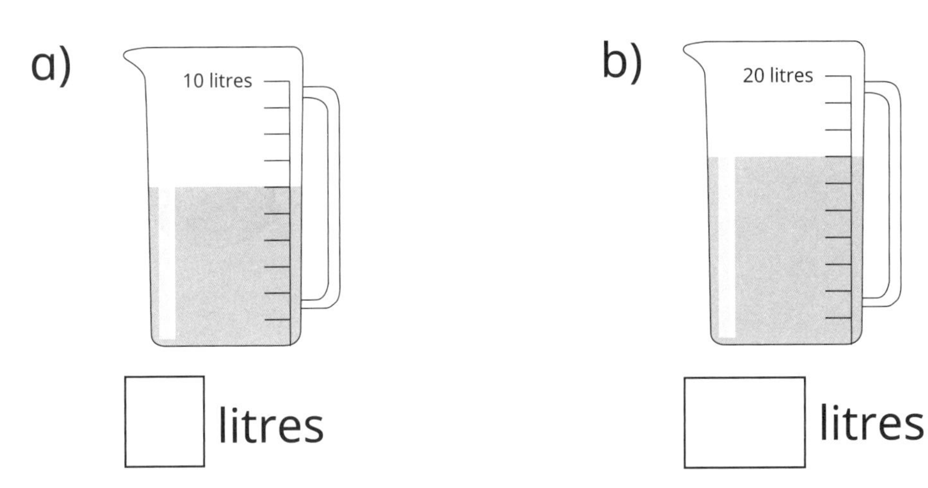

2 Three jugs each contain some water.

a) How much water is in each jug?

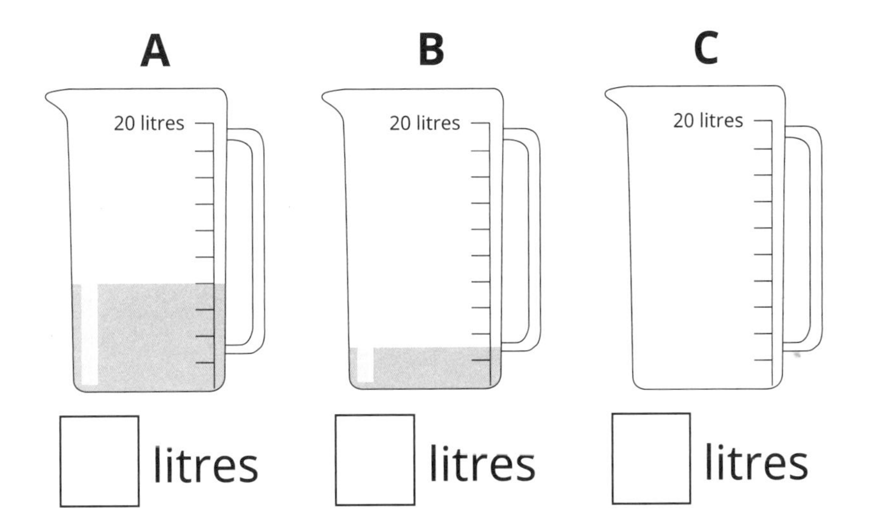

b) How much more water is in jug A than jug B?

☐ litres

c) The water from jug A and jug B is poured into jug C.

Draw on jug C to show where the water will reach.

3 What temperature is shown on each thermometer?

a)

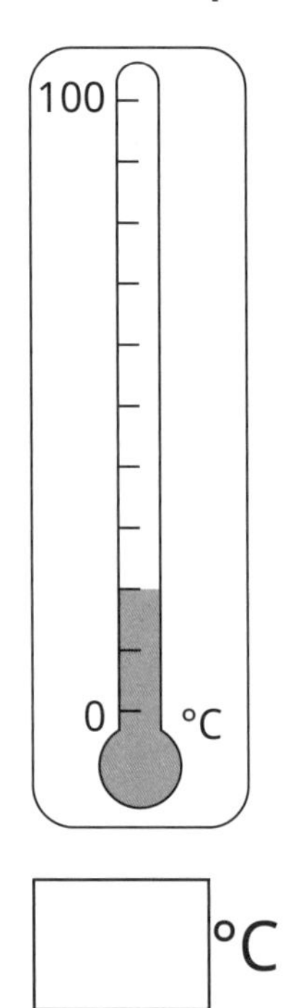

☐ °C

b)

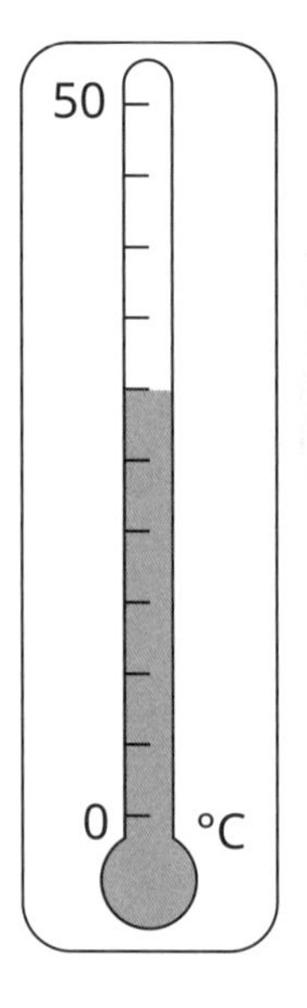

☐ °C

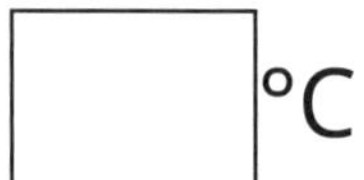

The **temperature** is how hot or cold something is. A **thermometer** measures the temperature.

4 Draw on the thermometers to show the temperatures.

a) 12 °C

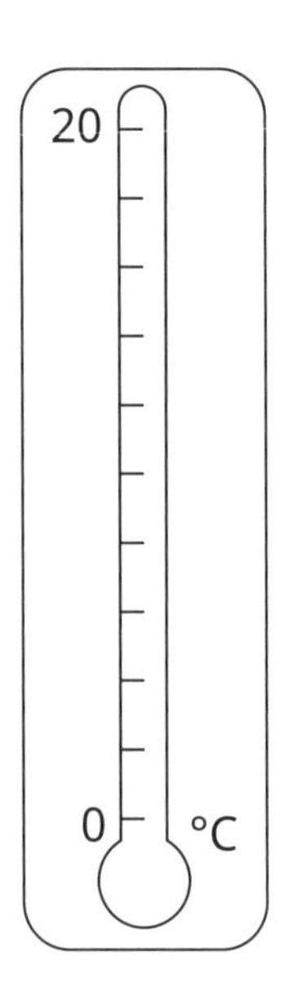

b) 25°C

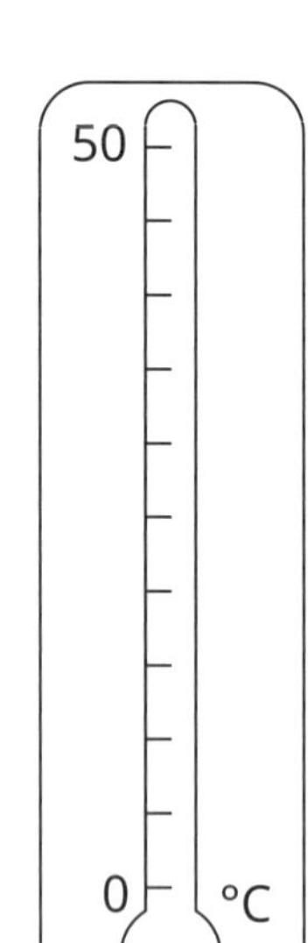

5 The capacity of a jug is 2 litres.
The capacity of a bucket is 5 litres.
How many jugs are needed to fill 4 buckets? ☐

Talk it out

Here are some containers.

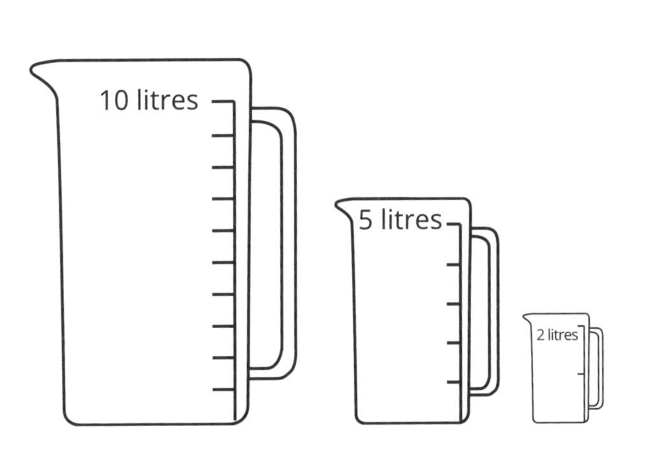

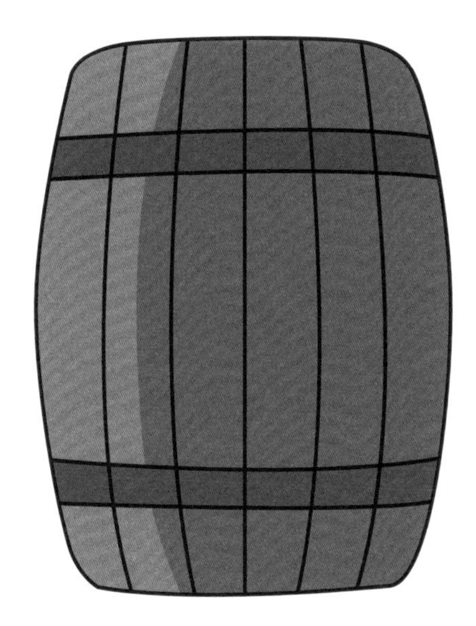

Ron wants to pour water into the barrel.

How do I pour exactly 43 litres of water?

Work out how Ron could use the jugs to fill the barrel.

How many different answers can you find?

Tell someone in your home.

First, Ron needs to …
Then he needs to …

How did you find these questions?   

Time to reflect

Look back through the work you have done this term. Think about what you enjoyed and what you found easy or hard. Talk about this to your teacher or someone at home.

Look back at the different coins and notes you saw on pages 45 and 46. How many can you name?

Sam has this much money.

She spends £1 and 65p.

How much money does she have left? £ ☐ and ☐ p

Circle one of the cards to show how you feel about solving problems with money.

1	2	3	4
I found these hard and need some help.	I need some more practice.	I can do these well and didn't make any mistakes.	I am confident and could teach someone else.

Use what you learned about the 2, 5 and 10 times-tables to answer the questions.

$3 \times 10 = \square$

$2 \times 10 = \square \times 5$

$\square = 7 \times 5$

$10 \times 4 = \square \times 5$

How can you share the counters into 4 equal groups? Write it as a division sentence.

☐ ÷ ☐ = ☐

Shade the face that describes best how you feel about multiplying and dividing.

I get it!

I need a little help.

I don't get it.

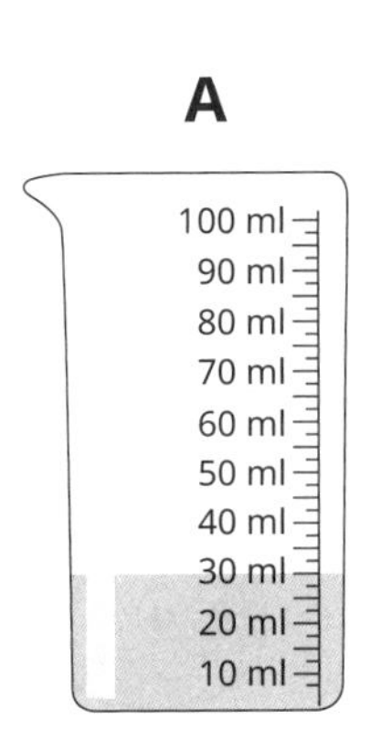

Look at page 79. Answer these capacity and volume questions.

What is the capacity of beaker A?

☐ ml

Dan pours the liquid from beaker B into beaker A.

What is the new volume of the water in beaker A?

☐ ml

Circle the statement that best shows how you feel about reading different scales.

I am confident and could teach someone else.	I think I understand but I need practice.	I don't understand and need help.

Have a think about all the work you've done this term. What went well? What do you still need to practise?

I am confident with ______________________________.

I will practise ______________________________.

Block 1 Fractions

In this block, we think about **fractions**. We talk about **halves**, **quarters** and **thirds**.

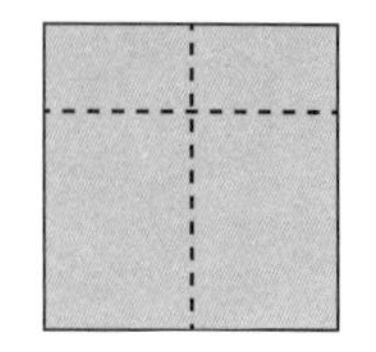

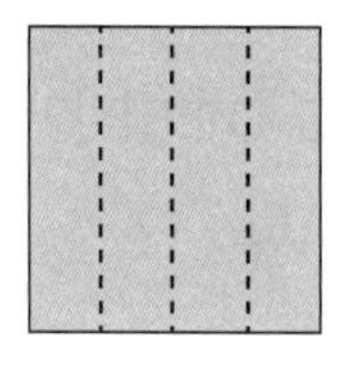

4 equal parts

The square is the whole. I can split the **whole** into **equal** and **unequal parts**.

Fractions are equal parts of a whole. We find half by splitting a whole into 2 equal parts. We find a quarter by splitting a whole into 4 equal parts. The whole here is 8. Half of 8 is 4. A quarter of 8 is 2

We start to record fractions using numerals. Here are the fractions, one third and three quarters.

A **unit fraction** has a numerator of 1

$\frac{1}{3}$ $\frac{3}{4}$

This is how many equal parts of the whole we have. It is called the **numerator**.

This is how many equal parts the whole is split into. It is called the **denominator**.

Here are some maths words that we see. What do they mean?

whole **part** **equal** **unequal** **fraction** **half** **quarter** **third** **numerator** **denominator** **equivalent**

Date:

Fractions

Let's practise

1 Here is the whole.

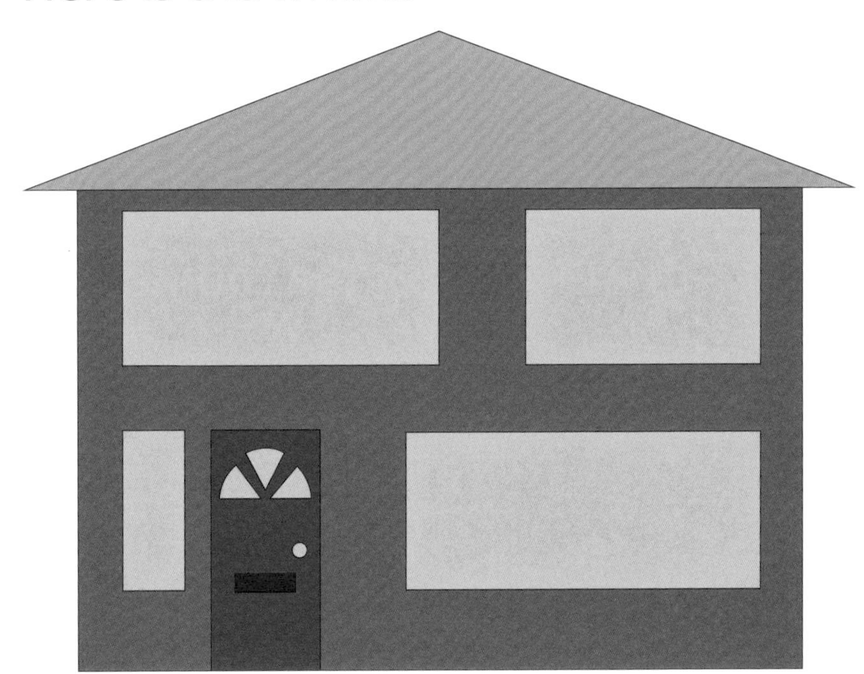

Tick the shapes that are a part of the whole.

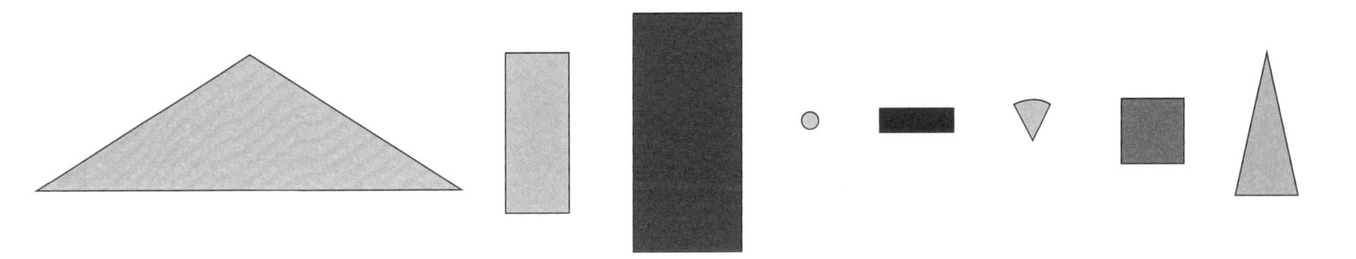

2 Tick the squares that are split into equal parts.

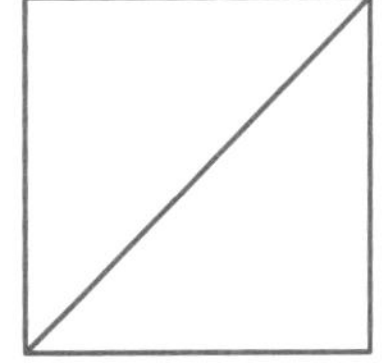
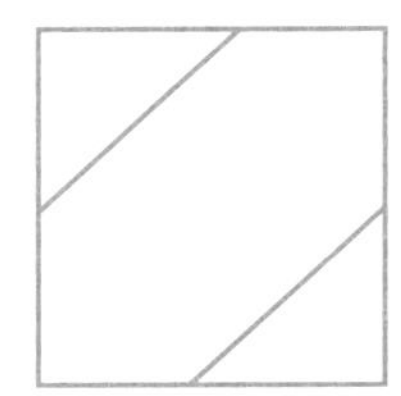
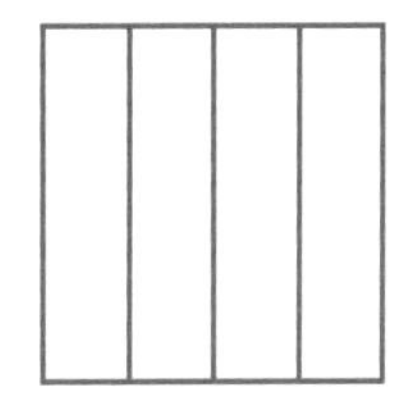

3 Split the rectangle in half in two different ways.

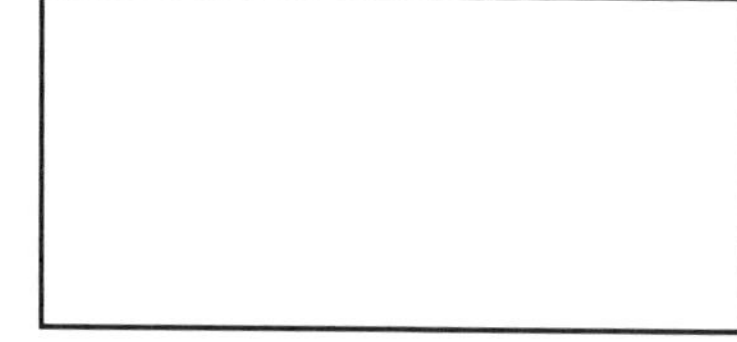

Make sure both parts are equal.

4 Here are some counters.

a) Circle $\frac{1}{2}$ of the counters.

b) What is $\frac{1}{2}$ of 20? 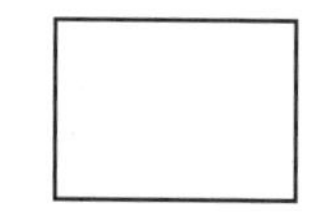

5 Complete the number sentences.

a) $\frac{1}{2}$ of 10 = ☐

b) $\frac{1}{2}$ of 8 = ☐

c) $\frac{1}{2}$ of ☐ = 6

d) $\frac{1}{2}$ of ☐ = 2

6 Shade $\frac{1}{4}$ of each shape.

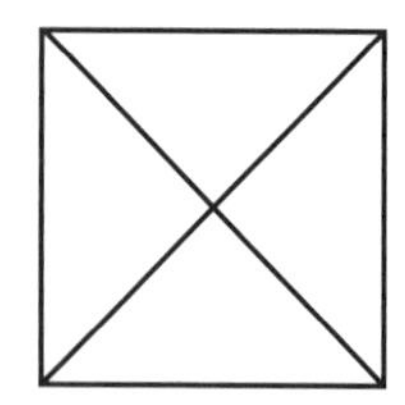
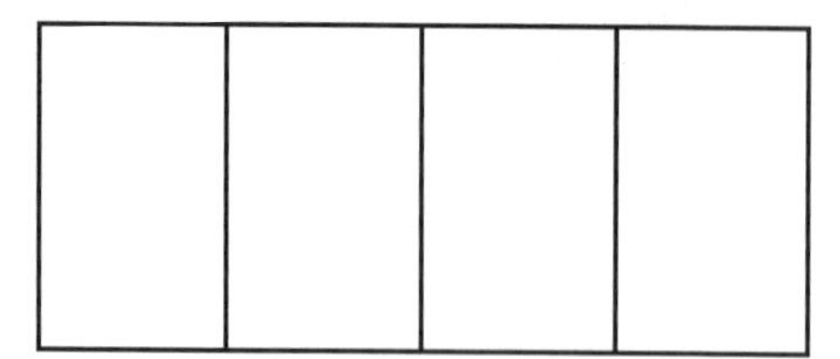
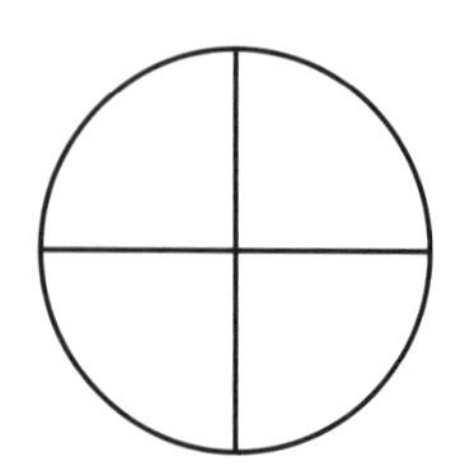
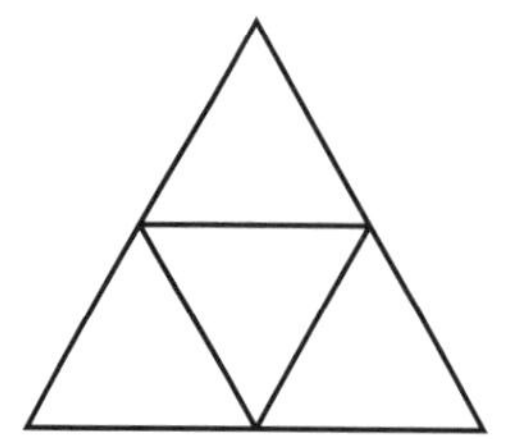

How do you know you have shaded one quarter?

Real world maths

Find 40 small objects around your home.

Use your objects to find $\frac{1}{2}$ of 40

How many equal parts did you split the objects into?

Talk it out

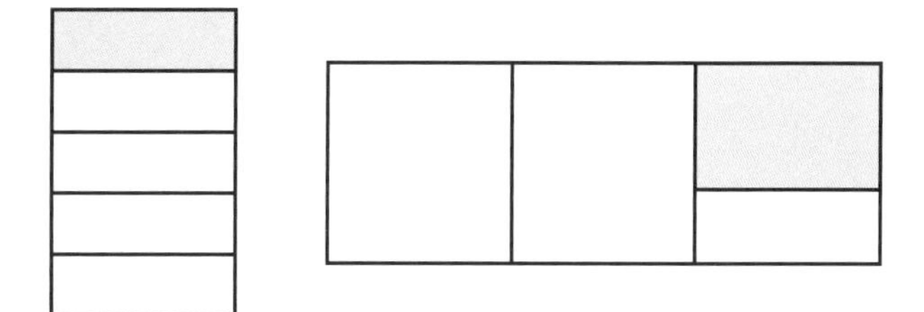

Each of these images shows one quarter.

Why is Tiny wrong?

Why might Tiny think that they show $\frac{1}{4}$?

Explain your answers to someone in your home.

Tiny is wrong because …

How did you find these questions?   

Fractions

Date:

Let's practise

1 Here are 32 counters.

a) Share the counters into 4 equal parts.

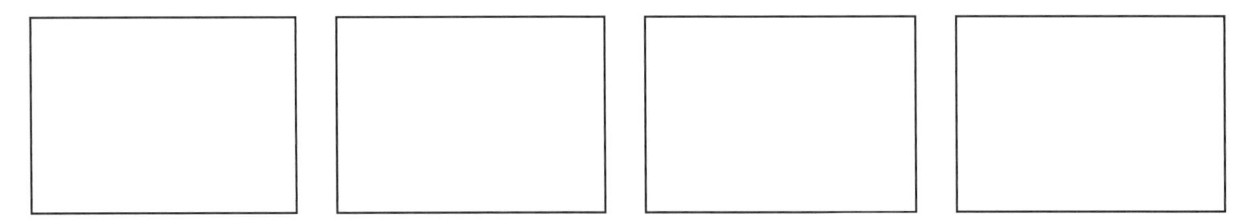

b) What is $\frac{1}{4}$ of 32? ☐

2 Tick the images that show $\frac{1}{3}$

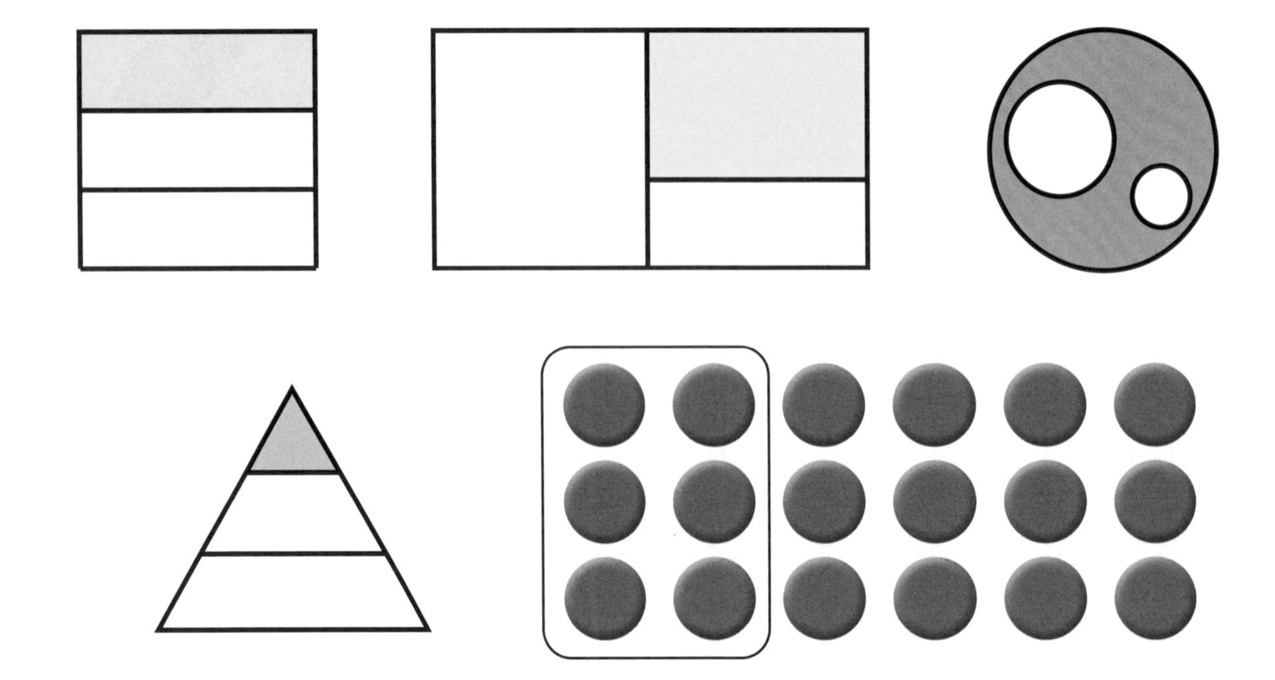

3 Here are some strawberries.

a) Circle to share the strawberries into 3 equal groups.

b) What is $\frac{1}{3}$ of 12? ☐

4 Complete the number sentences.

a) $\frac{1}{4}$ of 12 = ☐

b) $\frac{1}{3}$ of 15 = ☐

c) ☐ = $\frac{1}{4}$ of 24

d) $\frac{1}{3}$ of 24 = ☐

5 Complete the sentences.

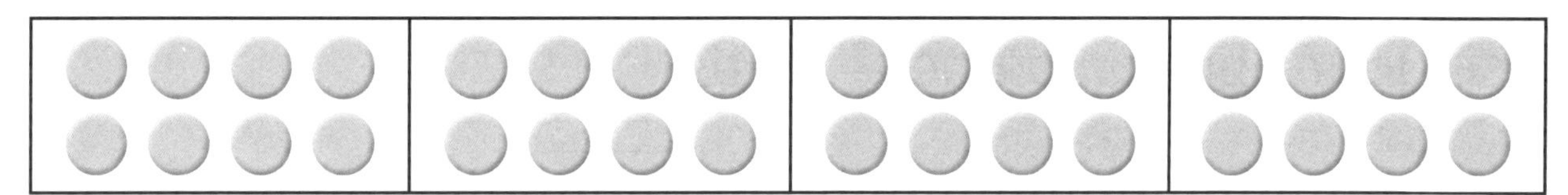

The whole has been split into ☐ equal parts.

Each part is worth ☐

The whole is ☐

6 Here are some fractions.

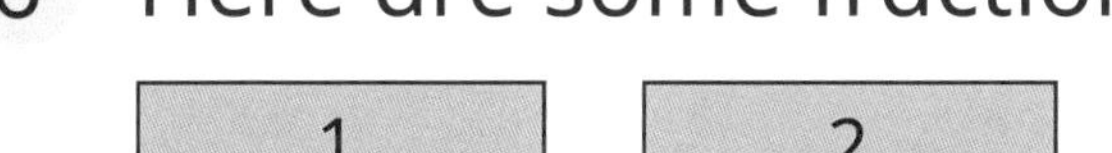

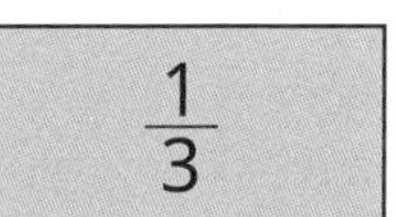
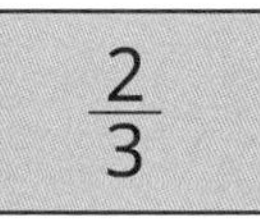
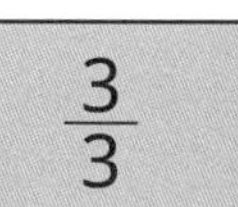

$\frac{1}{2}$ $\frac{2}{2}$ $\frac{1}{3}$ $\frac{2}{3}$ $\frac{3}{3}$

$\frac{1}{4}$ $\frac{2}{4}$ $\frac{3}{4}$ $\frac{4}{4}$

Circle the unit fractions.

How do you know? ______________________________

____

Real world maths

Find 48 small objects around your home, such as buttons.

Use your objects to find $\frac{1}{2}$ of 48 ☐

Use your objects to find $\frac{1}{4}$ of 48 ☐

Use your objects to find $\frac{1}{3}$ of 48 ☐

How did you do it? ______________________________

____

What do you notice? ______________________________

____

What happens to the parts when you split the whole into more equal groups?

____

____

How did you find these questions?   

Fractions

Date:

Let's practise

1 Shade the bar models to show the fractions.

a) $\frac{3}{4}$

b) $\frac{2}{3}$

c) $\frac{3}{5}$

d) $\frac{4}{4}$

What is the same about all the fractions?

2 Here are some counters.

a) Share the counters into 2 equal groups.

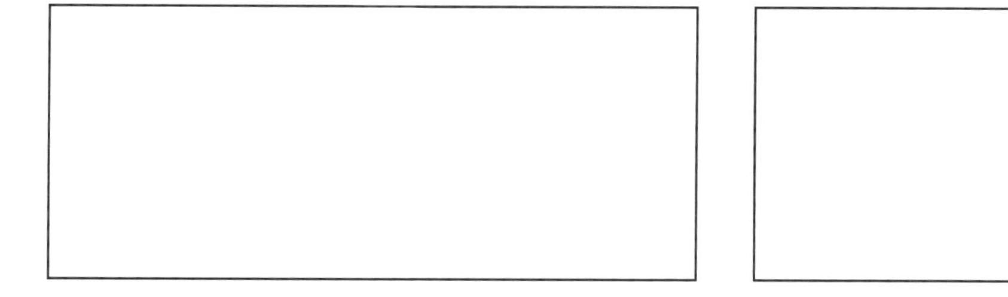

What is $\frac{1}{2}$ of 12?

b) Share the counters into 4 equal groups.

How many counters are there in 2 groups?

What is $\frac{2}{4}$ of 12?

What do you notice?

3 Shade the bar models to show the fractions.

a) $\frac{1}{2}$ 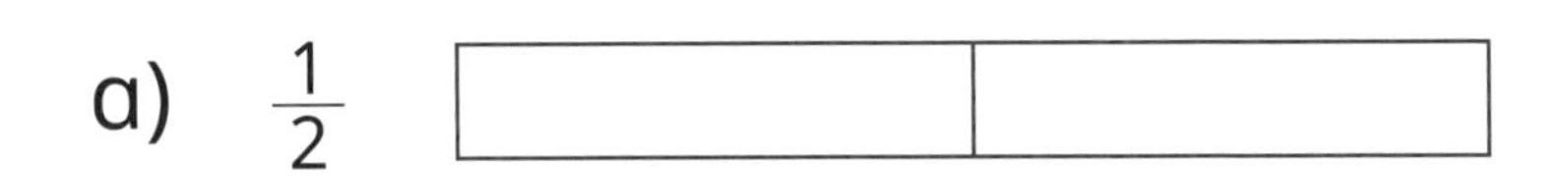

b) $\frac{2}{4}$ 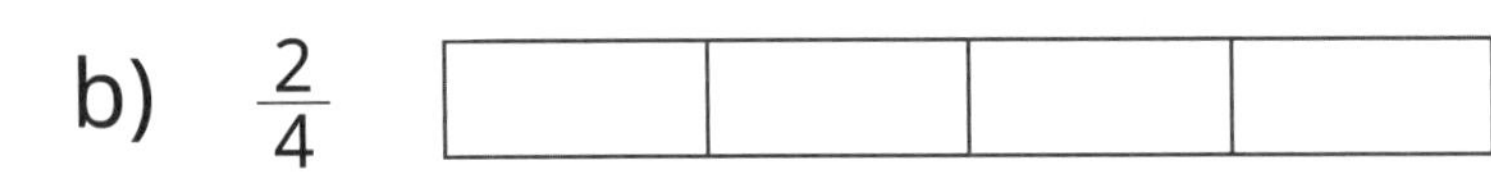

What do you notice?

4 Here are some coins.

a) Circle the coins to share them into 4 equal groups.

b) Use part a) of this question to complete the number sentences.

Can you spot any patterns?

$\frac{1}{4}$ of 20p = ☐ p $\frac{3}{4}$ of 20p = ☐ p

$\frac{2}{4}$ of 20p = ☐ p $\frac{4}{4}$ of 20p = ☐ p

5 Complete the number line.

How many parts are there? Which fraction will come next?

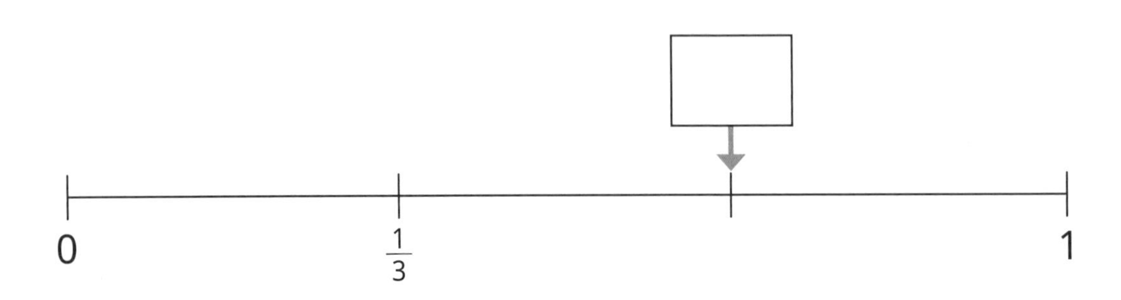

Find 16 of the same coin.

How much money do you have? ______

Share your coins into 4 equal groups.

If you don't have coins, imagine you have sixteen 1p, 5p or 10p coins.

Find $\frac{3}{4}$ of your amount.

$\frac{3}{4}$ of ______ = ______

Think it out

Tom has some sweets.

He puts $\frac{3}{4}$ of his sweets in a bag.

Here are the rest of the sweets.

How many sweets are in the bag? ☐

Draw a bar model to help you.

How did you find these questions?  

Block 2 Time

Do you remember how to tell the time to the **hour**? In this block, we also tell the time to the half hour and to 5 **minutes**.

Imagine splitting a clock face into 4 equal parts. This can help you to tell the time to the **quarter** hour.

On the hour

Quarter past the hour

Half past the hour

Quarter to the hour

You choose between using **past** and **to** when you say the time to 5 minutes. Up to 30 minutes, you say **past** the hour. After 30 minutes, you say **to** the hour.

We also think about how long different tasks take. Here are some time facts.

There are 60 seconds in 1 minute.
There are 60 minutes in 1 hour.
There are 24 hours in 1 day.

Here are some maths words that we see. What do they mean?

o'clock **hour hand** **minute hand** **half past** **quarter to**
quarter past **minute** **second** **hour** **day** **duration**

Time

Date:

Let's practise

1 What time is shown on each clock?

Use the word bank to help you.

o'clock	half past

a) 

____

c) 

____

b) 

____

d) 

____

2 Draw hands on the clocks to show the times.

a) 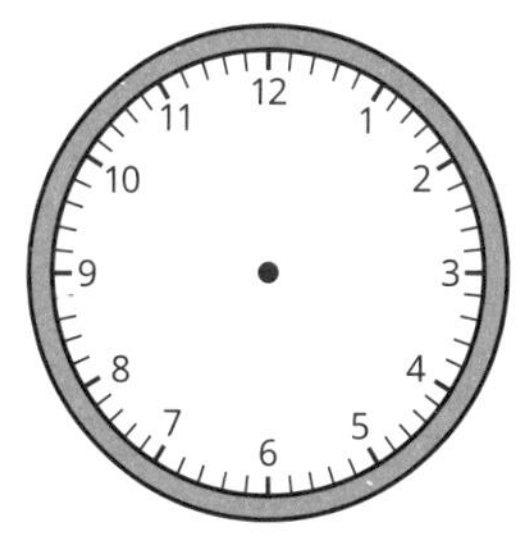

5 o'clock

c) 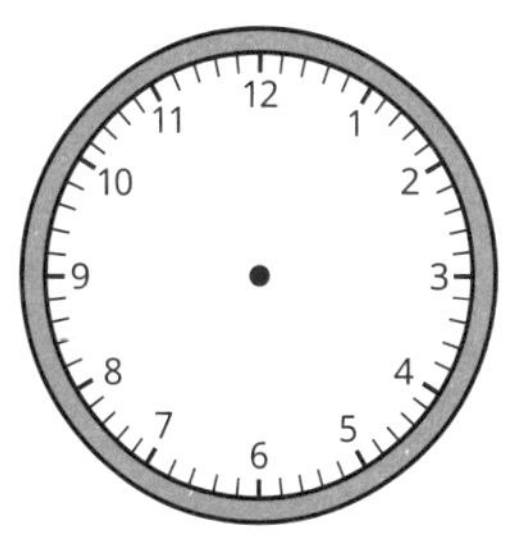

12 o'clock

b) 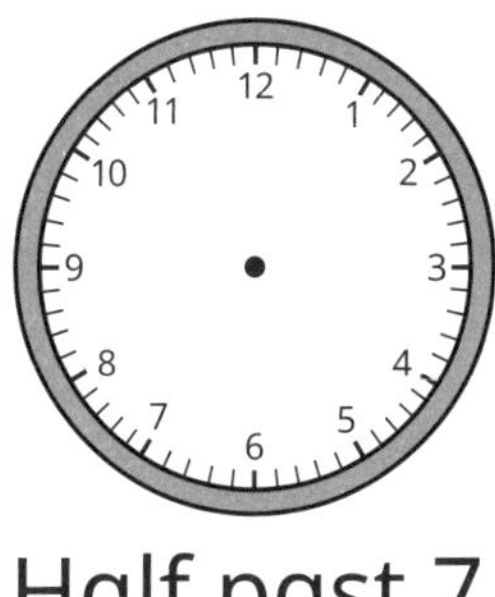

Half past 7

d) 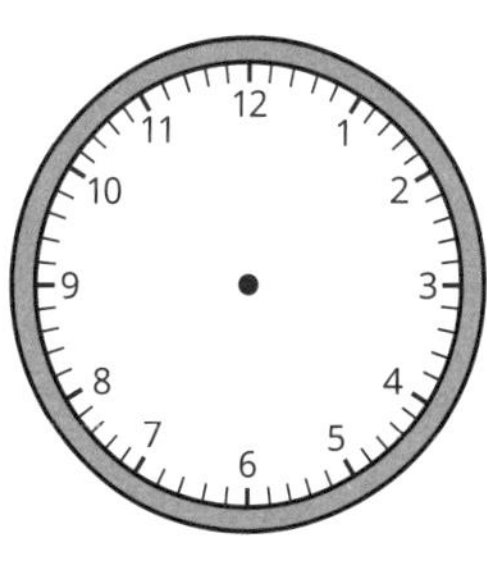

Half past 8

Remember, the minute hand is longer than the hour hand.

3 What time is shown on each clock?

Use the word bank to help you.

quarter to	quarter past

a) 

____

b) 

____

4 Draw hands on the clocks to show the times.

a) 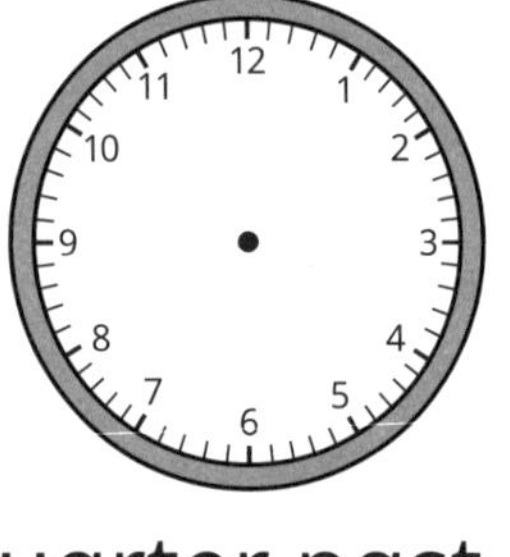

quarter past 3

b) 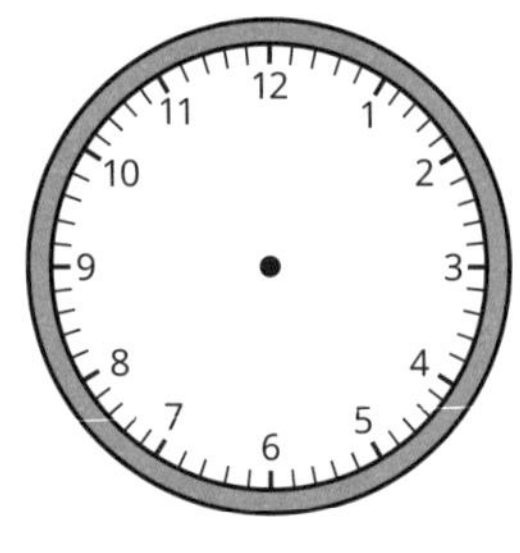

quarter to 10

Where does the minute hand point to at a quarter to or at a quarter past the hour?

5 Tiny made a clock, but all the numerals fell off.

I do not know what time it is!

How can Tiny still tell what time it is? ____________________

____

What time is it? ____________________

Max has made a pattern with clocks.

Draw the hands on the clocks to show the next 4 times in Max's pattern.

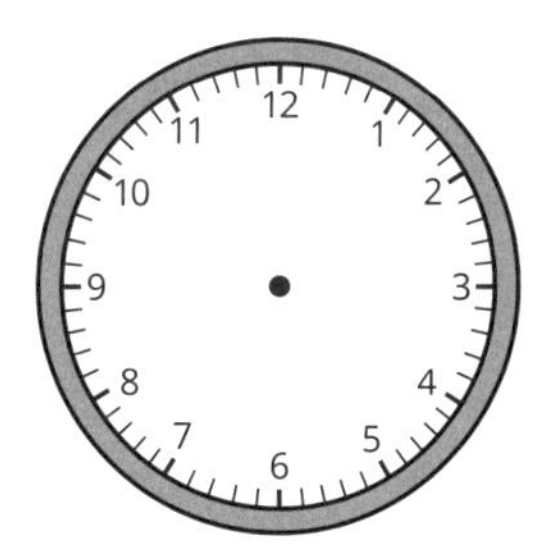 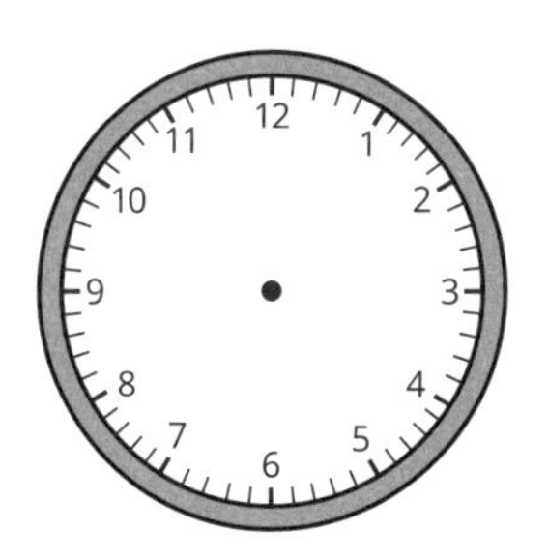 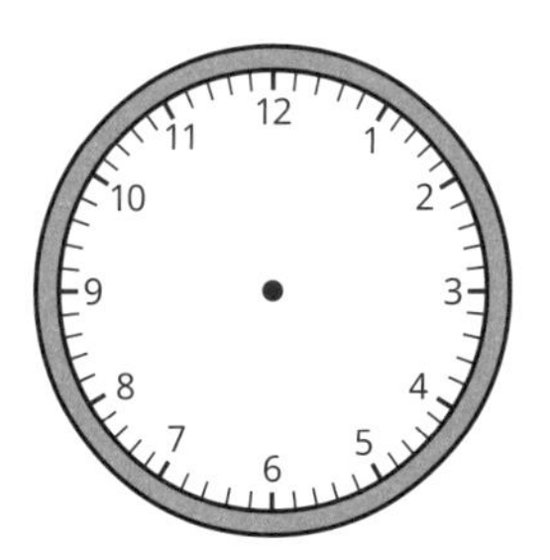 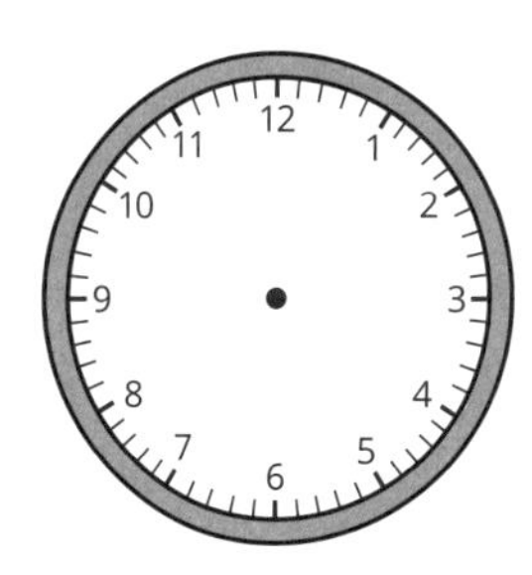

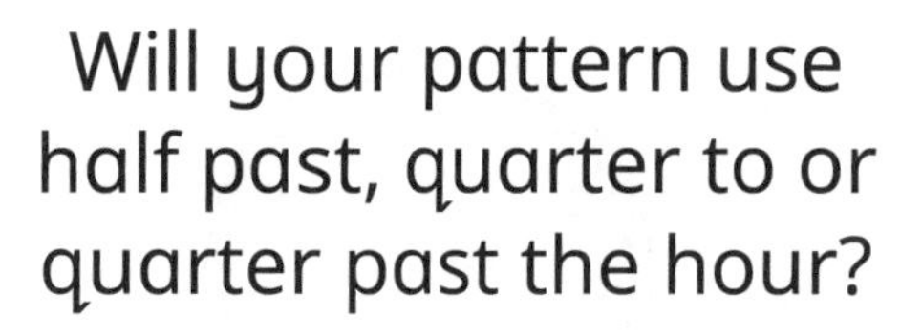

Create your own pattern using clocks.

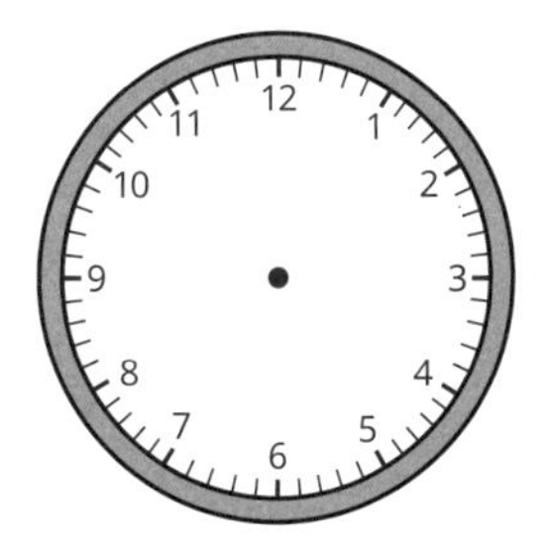 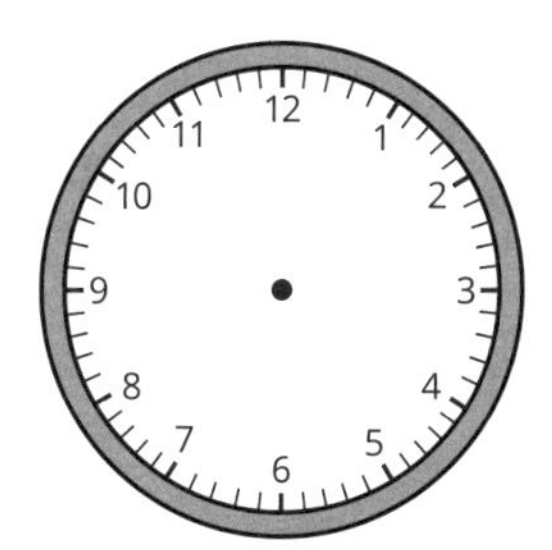 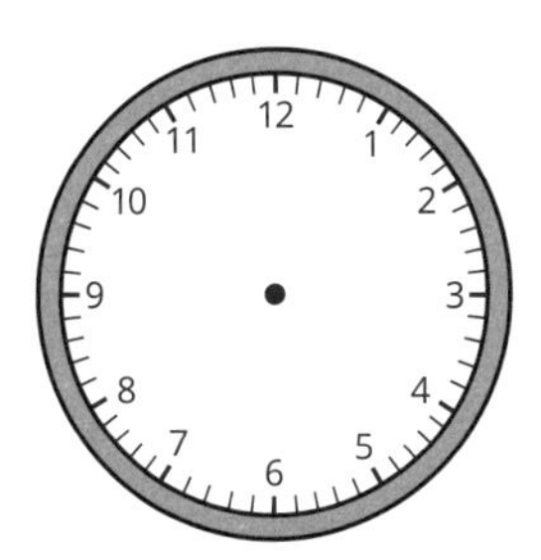 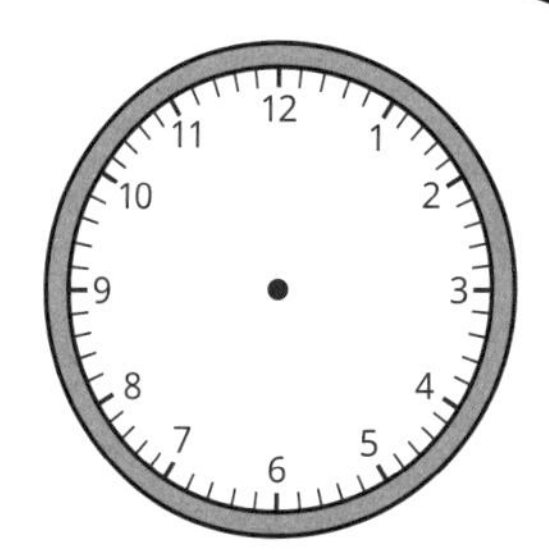

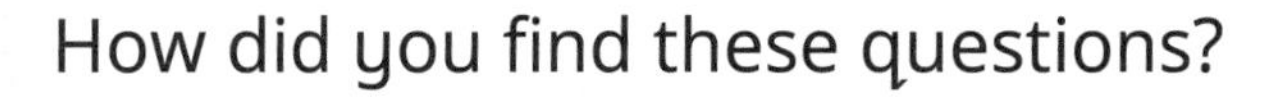

Time

Date:

Let's practise

1 What time is shown on each clock?

a) 

☐ minutes past ☐

b) 

☐ minutes past ☐

c) 

☐ minutes past ☐

d) 

☐ minutes past ☐

2 Draw hands on the clocks to show the times.

a) 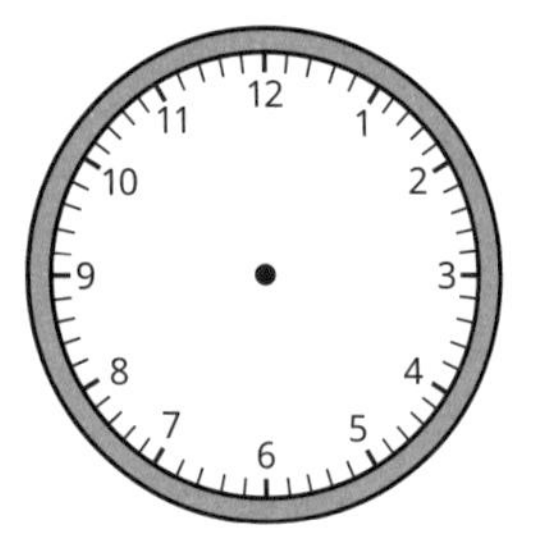

5 minutes past 11

b) 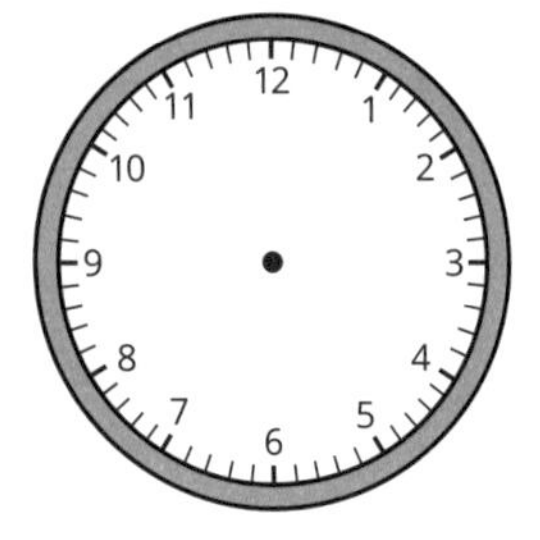

20 minutes past 4

c) 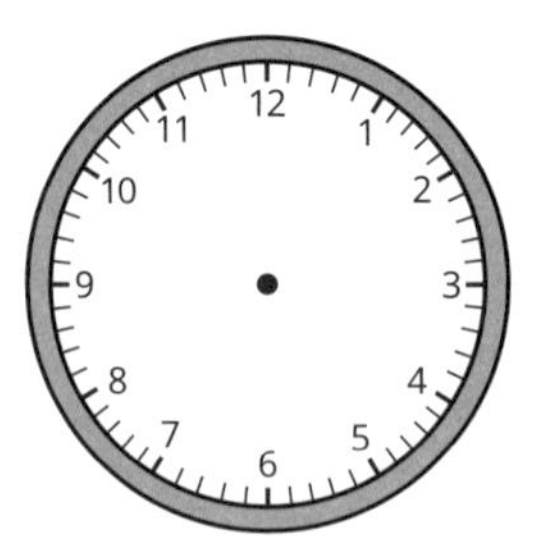

25 minutes past 6

d) 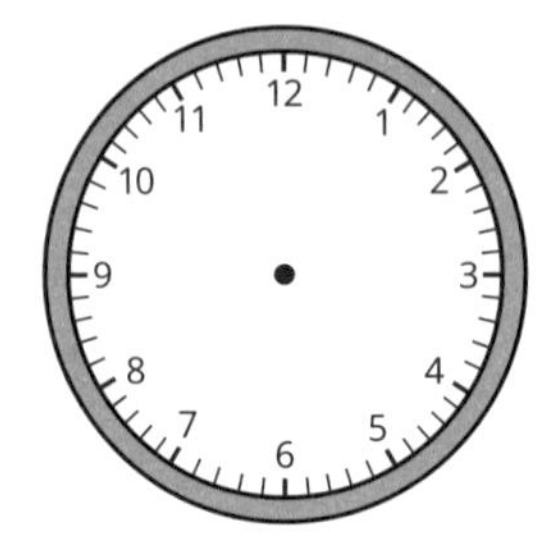

10 minutes past 8

3 What time is shown on each clock?

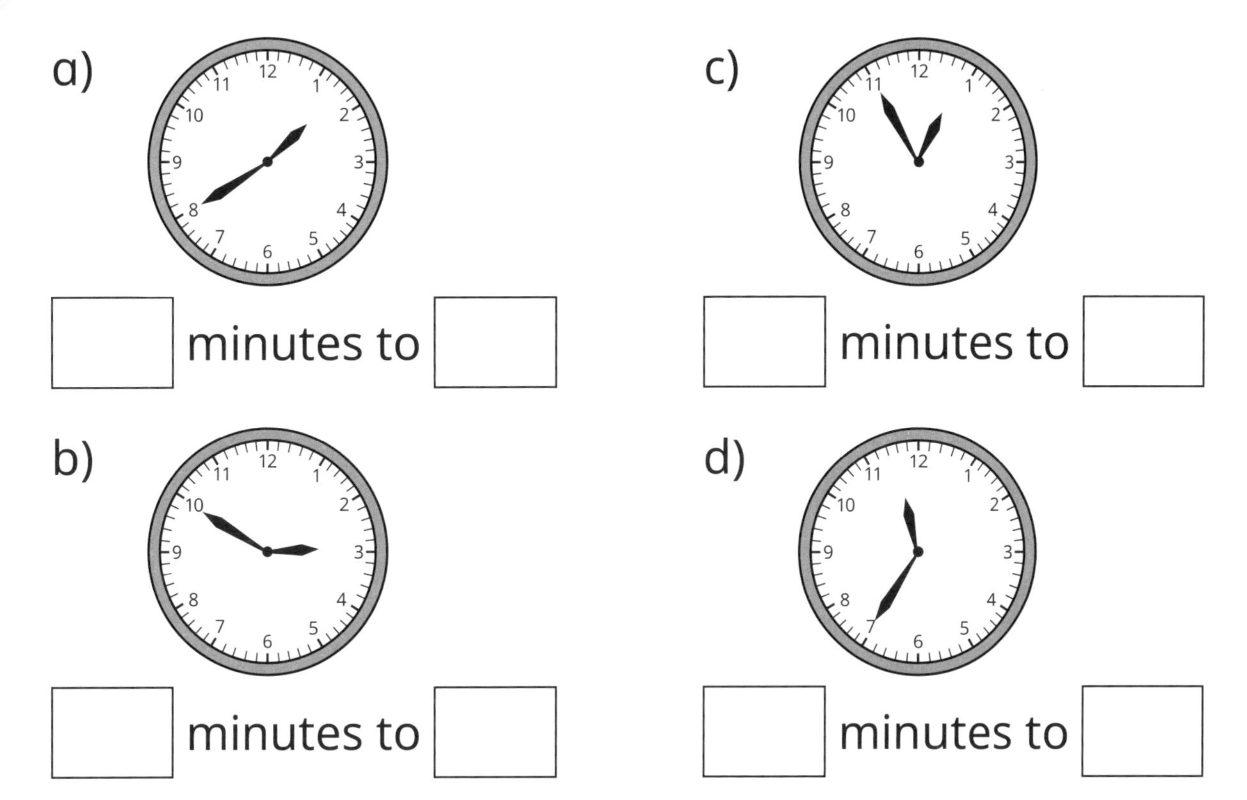

4 Write the time shown in 2 different ways.

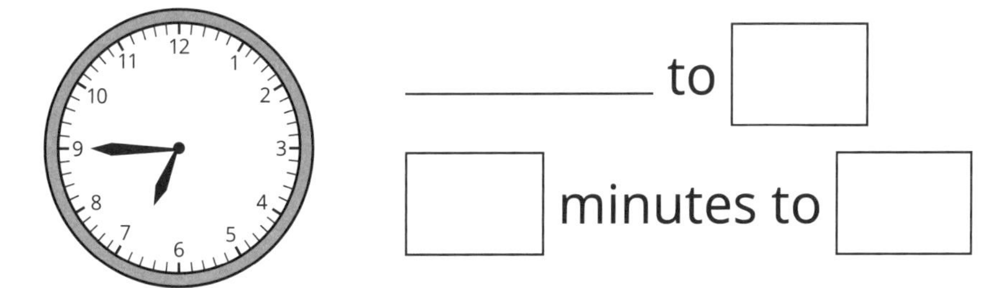

What other times can be written in more than one way?

____

5 Tiny is describing what time it is now.

5 minutes ago,
it was half past 4

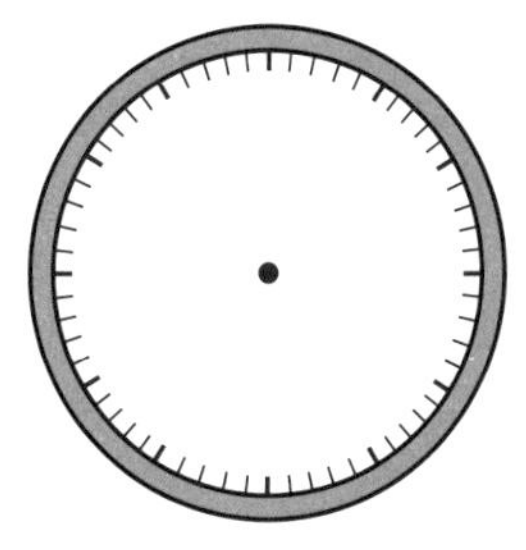

Draw hands on the clock to show the time now.

Talk it out

Write the numbers 1 to 12 on sticky notes.

Arrange them in a circle to look like a clock.

Use pencils as the hands on the clock.

I have made the time 4 o'clock.

Make a time.

Ask an adult what time it is.

Next, ask the adult to make a time.

Say the time they made.

What time have I made?

The time is …

How did you find these questions?  

Time

Date:

Let's practise

1 Complete the sentences.
Use the clocks to help you.

a) There are ☐ minutes in 1 hour.

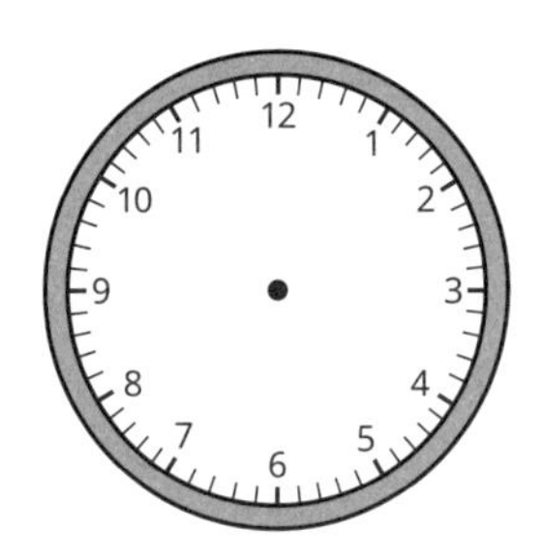

1 hour = ☐ minutes

b) There are ☐ minutes in half an hour.

$\frac{1}{2}$ hour = ☐ minutes

c) There are ☐ minutes in a quarter of an hour.

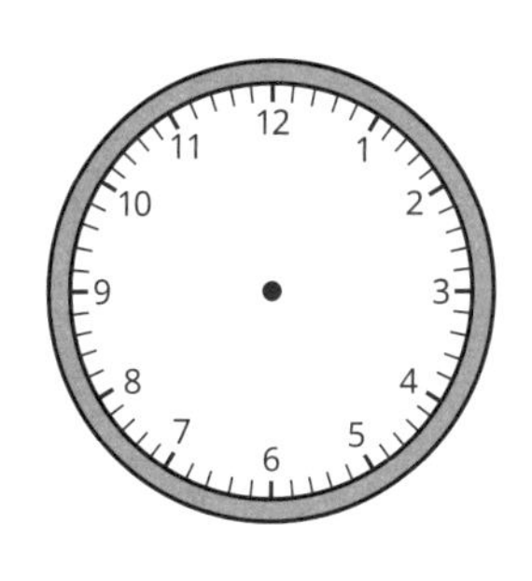

$\frac{1}{4}$ hour = ☐ minutes

d) There are ☐ minutes in three-quarters of an hour.

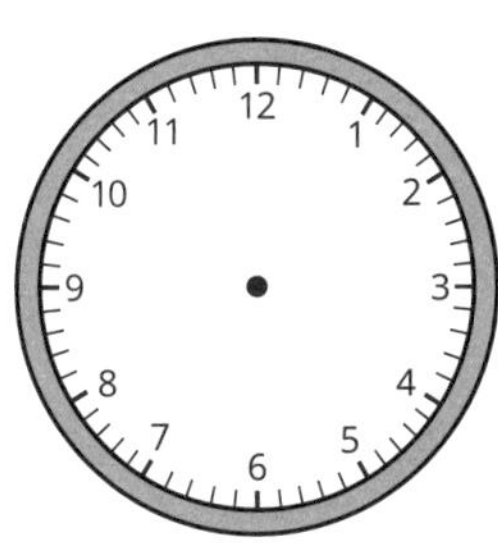

$\frac{3}{4}$ hour = ☐ minutes

2 Complete the sentences.

a) 1 hour 10 minutes = ☐ minutes

b) 1 hour 35 minutes = ☐ minutes

c) ☐ hour ☐ minutes = 75 minutes

d) 99 minutes = ☐ hour ☐ minutes

3

There are 60 hours in a day!

Tiny is talking about time.

Explain the mistake that Tiny has made.

____

____

4 Complete the sentences.

a) There are ☐ hours in 1 day.

b) There are ☐ hours in half a day.

c) There are ☐ hours in a quarter of a day.

d) There are ☐ hours in 2 days.

5 A football match lasts 90 minutes.

How long is the match in hours and minutes?

☐ hour and ☐ minutes

6 Use <, > or = to compare the durations of time.

a) hours in a day ◯ minutes in an hour

b) minutes in half an hour ◯ hours in 2 days

c) minutes in 1 hour 20 minutes ◯ 79 minutes

Think it out

Sam and Max both leave for school at this time.

Draw hands on the clocks to show the times Sam and Max arrive at school.

It takes me three quarters of an hour to get to school.

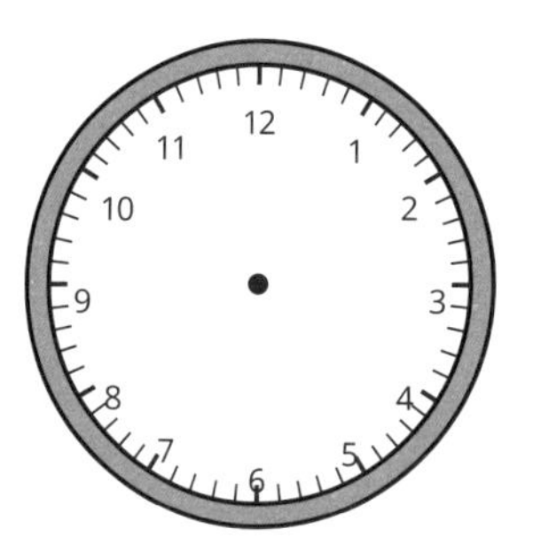

Sam

It takes me 50 minutes to get to school.

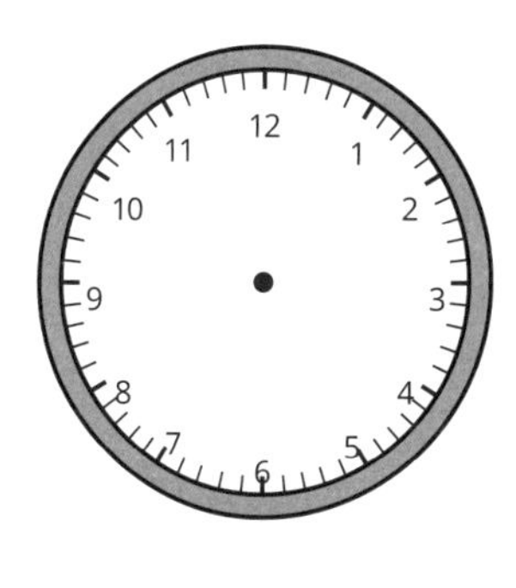

Max

Who arrives at school second? ______________________

How many minutes later do they arrive at school?

____

How did you find these questions?   

Block 3 Statistics

In this block, we look at different ways of presenting **data**.
Tables are a way of organising data into **rows** and **columns**.

I = 1 卌 = 5 One way of recording data is using **tally marks**.

Pictograms use pictures to show the data clearly. The **key** tells you how many children each circle represents. I can see that 4 more children walked on Friday than Thursday.

Day	Number of children in Year 2 who walked to school
Monday	●●●
Tuesday	●●●●●
Wednesday	●●●●●
Thursday	●●●●
Friday	●●●●●●

Key ● = 2 children

Block diagrams are another way we can represent the same data.
A block diagram has a clear **scale**. This one goes up in 2s.
Each block is worth 2

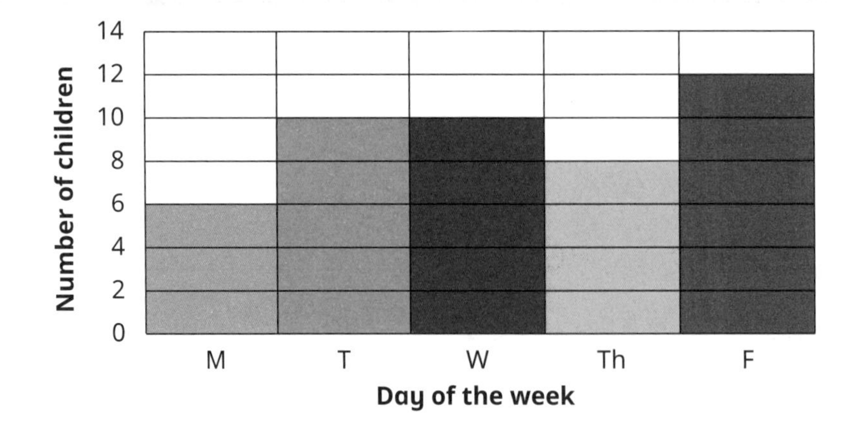

Here are some maths words that we see. What do they mean?

data **tally mark** **tally chart** **total** **pictogram**
key **block diagram** **scale** **label**

Statistics

Date:

Let's practise

1 Here is some fruit.

Complete the tally chart to show how many of each type of fruit there are.

Fruit	Tally	Total
Apple		
Banana		
Strawberry		
Pineapple		

2 Draw shapes to match the table.

Shape	Total
Square	2
Circle	4
Rectangle	1
Triangle	3

3 Whitney asks people what their favourite pet is.
She records the data she collects in a table.

Pet	Tally	Total
Dog	𝍸	5
Cat	𝍸 IIII	9
Rabbit	III	3
Fish	𝍸 I	6
Snake	II	2

a) How many people said a cat was their favourite pet? ☐

b) How many more people said fish than rabbit? ☐

c) How many people did Whitney ask altogether? ☐

d) Complete the block diagram to display the data in the table.

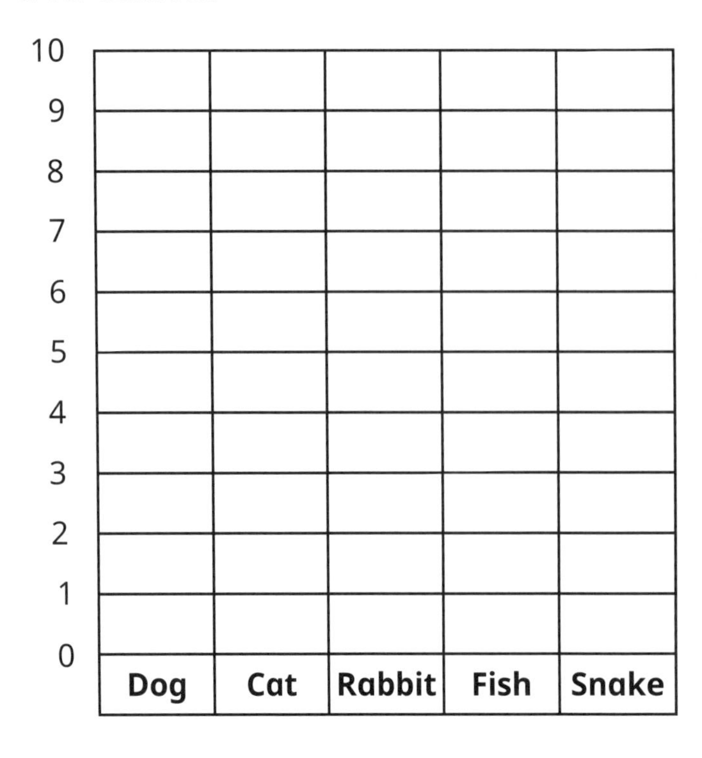

A **block diagram** is a way of presenting data using coloured blocks.

Real world maths

Find some items around your home.

Remember to draw your tally marks in neat groups of 5

Tally how many of each item you have.

Item	Tally	Total

Draw a block diagram to match the table.

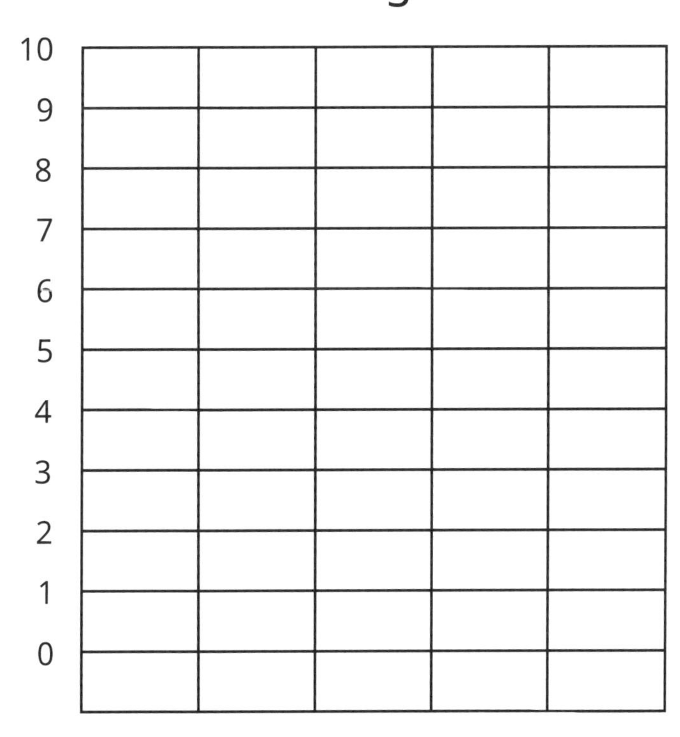

How many blocks will you need to colour in for each item?

How did you find these questions?

Statistics

Date:

Let's practise

1 The pictogram shows the favourite pizza topping of some people.

Remember, a **pictogram** is a chart that uses pictures or symbols to represent data.

Topping	Number of people
Cheese	
Tomato	
Chicken	
Mushroom	
Other	

Key
= 1 person

a) How many people said cheese? ☐

b) How many people said mushroom? ☐

c) How many more people said chicken than tomato?

☐

d) Which 2 toppings had the same number of votes?

________________ and ________________

e) How many people were asked in total? ☐

2 The pictogram shows how many tubs of different ice cream flavours were served at a party.

Remember to use the **key** to know how many tubs each square represents.

Flavour	Number of tubs
Vanilla	■ ■ ■
Chocolate	■ ■ ■ ■ ■ ▌
Strawberry	■ ■ ■ ■
Banana	■ ■
Other	■ ■ ■ ■ ▌

Key

■ = 2 tubs

a) How many tubs of strawberry were served? ☐

b) How many tubs of chocolate were served? ☐

c) How many more tubs of other flavours were served than banana? ☐

d) How many fewer tubs of vanilla were served than chocolate? ☐

e) How many tubs were served in total? ☐

Think it out

Dora's family orders a fruit box.

There are 10 apples in the box.

There are half as many pears as apples.

The number of oranges is double the number of apples.

There are 5 fewer bananas than oranges.

There are twice as many peaches as bananas.

Complete both pictograms to show how many pieces of each fruit are in the box.

Fruit	Number of pieces of fruit
Apple	
Pear	
Orange	
Banana	
Peach	

Key
● = 5 pieces of fruit

Fruit	Number of pieces of fruit
Apple	
Pear	
Orange	
Banana	
Peach	

Key
● = 10 pieces of fruit

What is the same about your pictograms? What is different?

Explain what you notice to an adult.

How did you find these questions?   

Block 4 Position and direction

In this block, we follow and give **directions** and describe **position** using words like **above**, **between**, **to the left**, and **to the right**.

We describe turns. There can be more than one answer, depending on which direction you turn. You can turn **clockwise** or **anti-clockwise**.

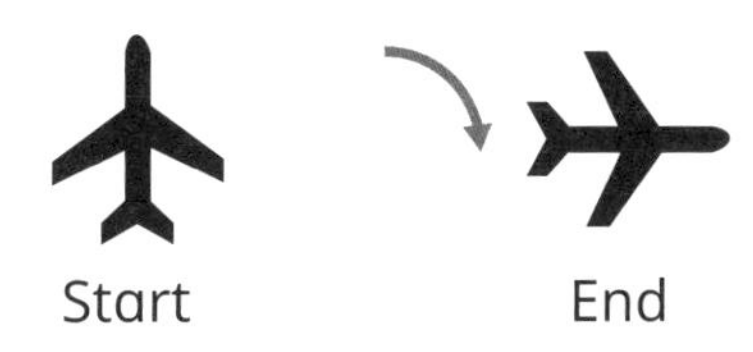

The plane has made a **quarter turn** clockwise.

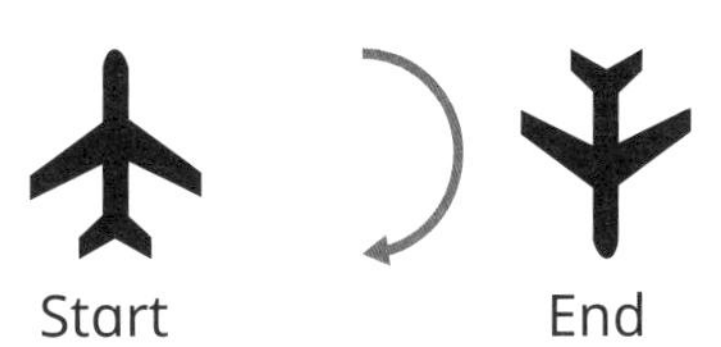

The plane has made a **half turn** clockwise.

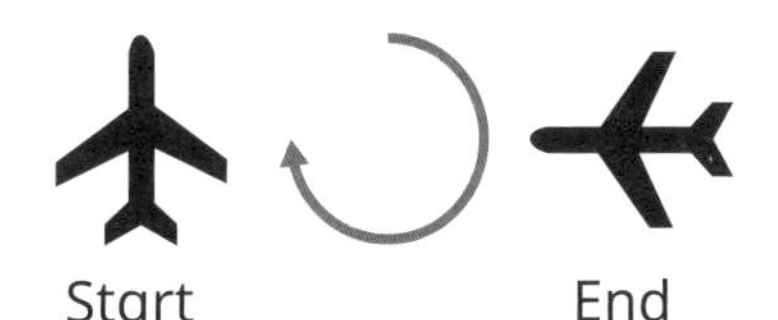

The plane has made a **three-quarter turn** clockwise.

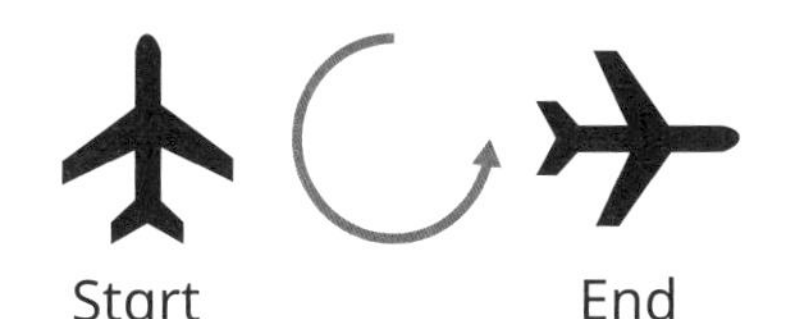

The plane has made a three-quarter turn anti-clockwise.

We look at objects on a grid and describe their **movement**. Remember to think about what way the object is facing. The bear moves 3 squares forwards. Then, it makes a quarter turn anti-clockwise and moves another 3 squares **forwards**.

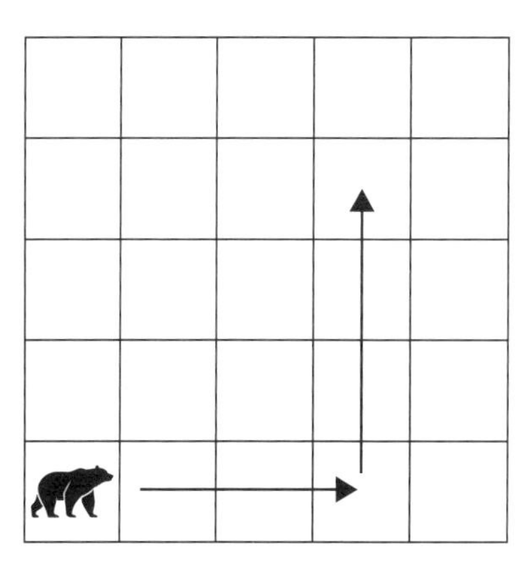

Here are some maths words that we see. What do they mean?

forwards **backwards** **up** **down** **left** **right** **route** **direction** **position** **movement** **clockwise** **anti-clockwise** **quarter turn** **half turn** **three-quarter turn** **whole turn** **pattern**

Position and direction

Date:

Let's practise

1 Here are some shapes.

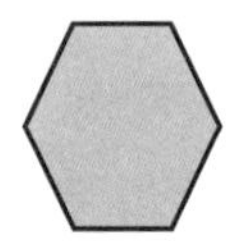    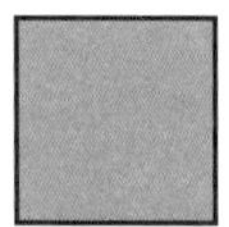

Use the word bank to complete the sentences.

left	right

a) The circle is to the ______________ of the pentagon.

b) The square is to the ______________ of the triangle.

c) The hexagon is to the ______________ of the circle.

d) The square is to the ______________ of the hexagon.

2 Here are some fruits.

Use the word bank to complete the sentences.

above	below

a) The apple is ______________ the banana.

b) The pear is ______________ the apple.

c) The pineapple is ______________ the banana.

d) The pear is ______________ the strawberry.

3 Some shapes are drawn on a grid.

Follow the directions and draw the shapes in their new positions.

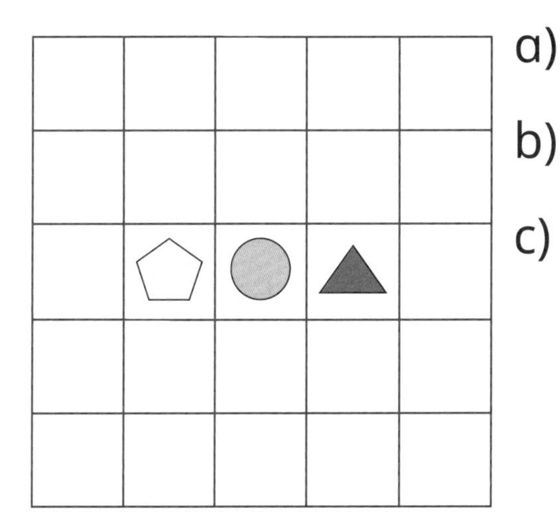

a) Circle: 2 squares left

b) Pentagon: 2 squares down

c) Triangle: 2 squares up and 1 square right

4 Draw a new arrow to show the turns.

a) A quarter turn clockwise

b) A quarter turn anti-clockwise

c) A half turn

d) A three-quarter turn clockwise

Think it out

Describe 2 different paths the ant can take to get to the star.

Use the word bank to help you.

forwards	backwards	left	right

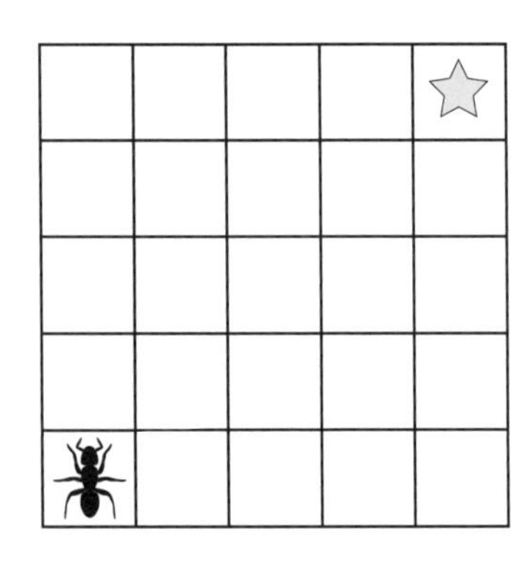

Remember to think about which way the ant is facing.

Path 1:

____

Path 2:

____

Talk it out

It doesn't matter if I turn a half turn clockwise or anti-clockwise, I'll be facing the same way.

Explain why Tiny is right.

Draw the turns to help you explain.

Tiny is right because . . .

How did you find these questions?   

Position and direction

Date:

Let's practise

1 Tiny wants to get to the pear.

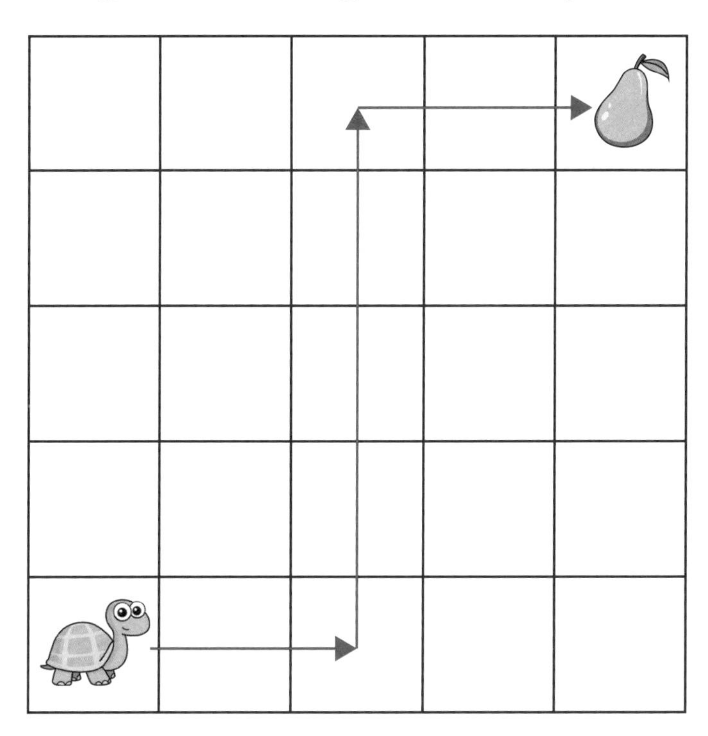

Use the word bank to complete the sentences to describe Tiny's path.

forwards	backwards	quarter turn
half turn	clockwise	anti-clockwise

First, Tiny walks 2 squares ______________.

Then, Tiny makes a ______________

______________.

Then, Tiny walks 4 squares ______________.

Then, Tiny makes a ______________

______________.

Then, Tiny walks 2 squares ______________ to get to the pear.

2 Describe 2 different routes from A to B.
Use the word bank to help you.

up	left
down	right

A				
				B

Route 1: ______________________________

____

Route 2: ______________________________

____

3 Draw the next 2 shapes in each pattern.

a) 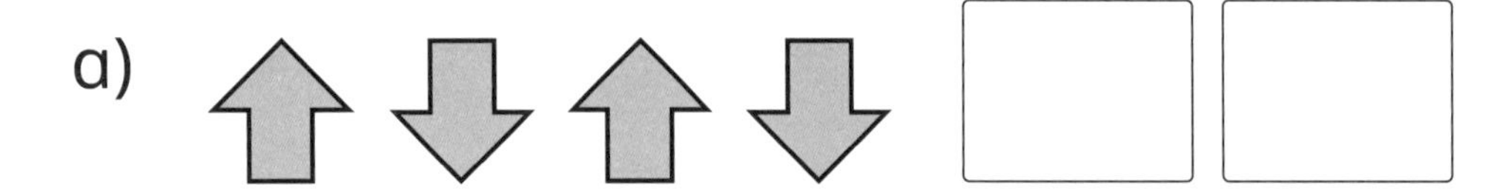

b) 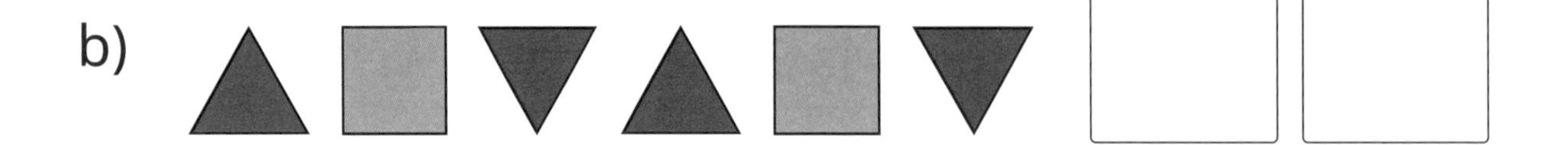

c) 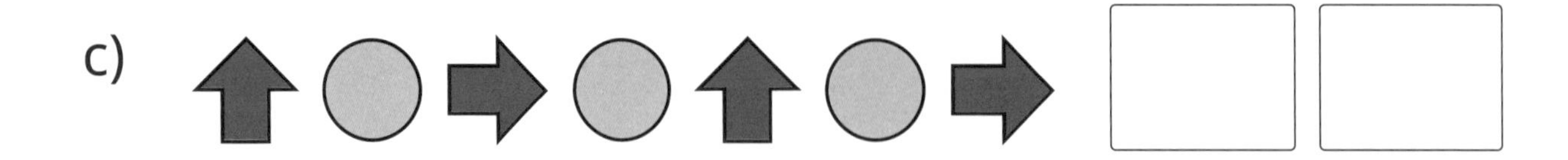

d) 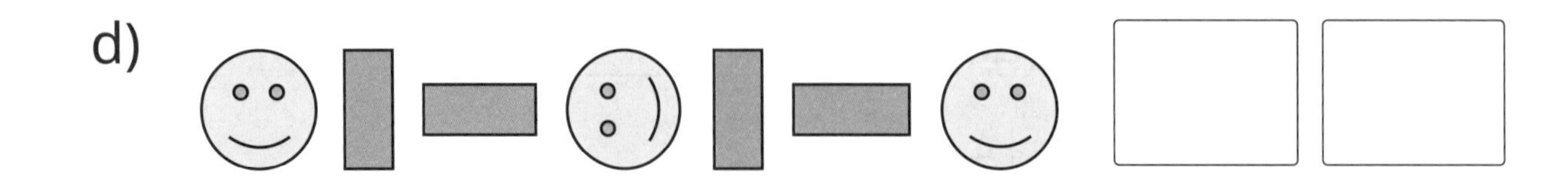

Talk it out

Draw your own grid using chalk on pavement, for example.

Put a figure or a stuffed animal on your grid.

Describe different paths for your figure or stuffed animal to take.

Tell someone the start and end points.

See if they can guess your path.

My figure moved … squares right and … squares down.

My teddy started here and ended here. What was its path?

Think it out

Describe 2 different routes from the shop to the park.

You must also visit the house and the pool each time.

Route 1: ______________________

____

____

Route 2: ______________________

____

____

How did you find these questions?

Consolidation

Date:

Let's practise

1 Circle $\frac{1}{4}$ of each set of objects.

a)

b)

c)

d)

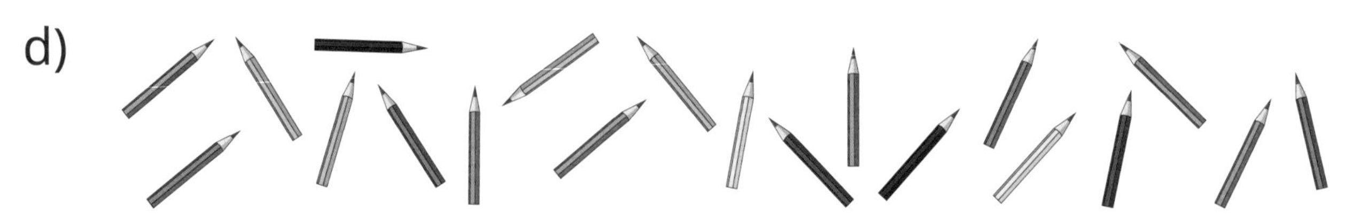

2 Complete the number sentences.

a) $\frac{1}{4}$ of 8 = ☐

b) $\frac{1}{4}$ of 24 = ☐

c) ☐ = $\frac{1}{4}$ of 12

d) $\frac{1}{4}$ of ☐ = 5

3 Complete the number sentences.

a) $\frac{3}{4}$ of 8 = ☐

b) $\frac{3}{4}$ of 24 = ☐

c) ☐ = $\frac{3}{4}$ of 12

d) $\frac{3}{4}$ of 20 = ☐

4 What time is shown on each clock?

a) 

____

c) 

____

b) 

____

d) 

____

5 Max has 27 sweets.

He gives $\frac{1}{3}$ of his sweets to Jo.

a) How many sweets does Max give Jo?

[ ]

b) How many sweets does Max have left?

6 Ron has some 10p coins.

Draw a bar model to help you.

He gives $\frac{3}{4}$ of his 10p coins to Sam.

He has 20p left.

How much money did he give to Sam?

[ ] p

Think it out

Tommy gets to football training at this time.

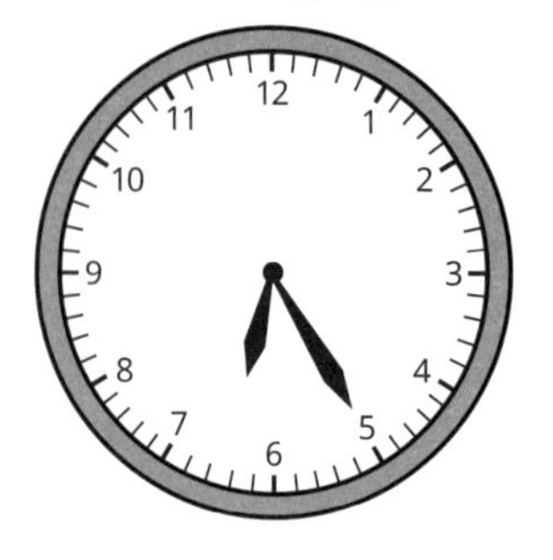

How many minutes are in an hour?

He trains for 95 minutes.

It takes 25 minutes to get home.

Draw hands on the clock to show the time that Tommy gets home.

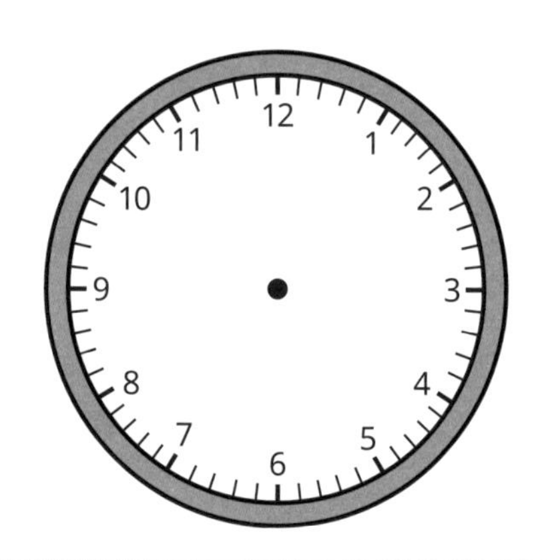

Talk it out

Why is 15 minutes past the hour the same as quarter past the hour?

Why is 30 minutes past the hour the same as half past the hour?

Why is 45 minutes past the hour the same as quarter to the next hour?

Share your answers with an adult.

15 minutes past is the same as quarter past because …

There are 60 minutes in an hour, so …

How did you find these questions?   

Consolidation

Date:

Let's practise

1 Kim has emptied her kitchen cupboard.

a) Complete the tally chart to show how many of each food item were in the cupboard.

Food item	Tally	Total
Cereal		
Tomatoes		
Rice		
Pasta		
Beans		

b) Use your tally chart to complete the block diagram.

10					
9					
8					
7					
6					
5					
4					
3					
2					
1					
0	Cereal	Tomatoes	Rice	Pasta	Beans

2 Use the word bank to complete the sentences.

to the left of	to the right of	above	below

a) The smiley face is ______________________________ ______________________________ the octagon.

b) The pentagon is ____________________ the rectangle.

c) The triangle is ____________________ the hexagon.

d) The square is ______________________________ ____________________ the rectangle.

3 Describe 2 paths the bee can use to get to the hive.

Path 1: ____________________
____
____

Path 2: ____________________
____
____

Real life maths

Cut some triangles and rectangles out of paper.

Use your triangles and rectangles to make a pattern.

Describe your pattern to an adult.

Ask them to continue your pattern.

Turn the shapes in your pattern.

My pattern uses …

The pattern repeats …

Talk it out

What is different about **clockwise** and **anti-clockwise**?

Why do you think they are called that?

I think clockwise means …

I wonder if it's anything to do with a clock.

I think anti-clockwise means …

They are different because …

How did you find these questions?    

Time to reflect

Look back through your work this term. Think about what you enjoyed and what you found easy or hard. Talk about this with your teacher or someone at home.

Look back at Block 1 and think about unit and non-unit fractions. (Unit fractions have a numerator of 1) Use what you know to solve this problem.

Kim takes $\frac{3}{4}$ of the marbles.

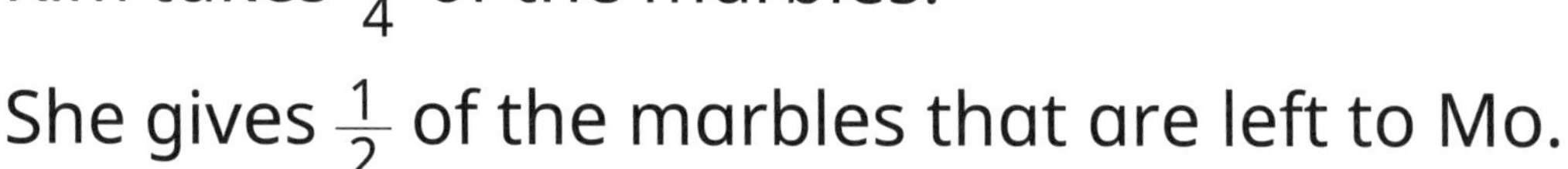

She gives $\frac{1}{2}$ of the marbles that are left to Mo.

How many marbles does she give to Mo?

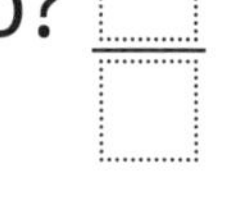

Shade the face that best shows how confident you are working with fractions.

I get it!

I need a little help.

I don't get it.

Write the time in words and show it on the clock.

Alex arrived at school at a quarter to 9

She read her book for 25 minutes.

At what time did she stop reading? ______________

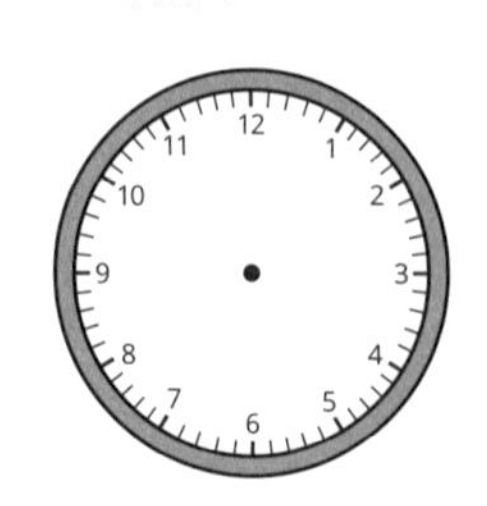

Circle the statement that best shows how you feel about telling the time.

I am confident and could teach someone else.	I think I understand but I need practice.	I don't understand and need help.

Think about all you know about pictograms and answer the questions.

The pictogram shows how much money four Year 2 classes raised for charity.

Class	Money in pounds
2L	■ ■ ■ ■
2C	■ ■ ■ ■ ■ ■
2T	■ ■
2P	■ ■ ■ ■ ■ ■ ■

Key ■ = £5

a) Which class raised the most money? ______________

b) How much more money did 2C raise than 2L? £ ☐

c) Which class raised £25 less than 2P? ______________

Circle the card that describes best how confident you are with using and making pictograms.

1	2	3	4
I found these hard and need some help.	I need some more practice.	I can do these well and didn't make any mistakes.	I am confident and could teach someone else.

Look back through your work on position and direction in Block 4. Tell an adult about some of the words you use when you give directions.

Dora moves the counter 2 squares left, 1 square down and 3 squares right.

Draw a circle on the grid to show where the counter is now.

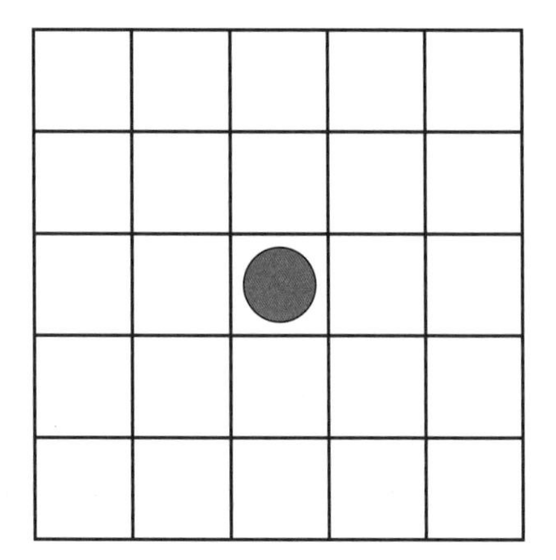

Draw the next 2 shapes in this pattern.

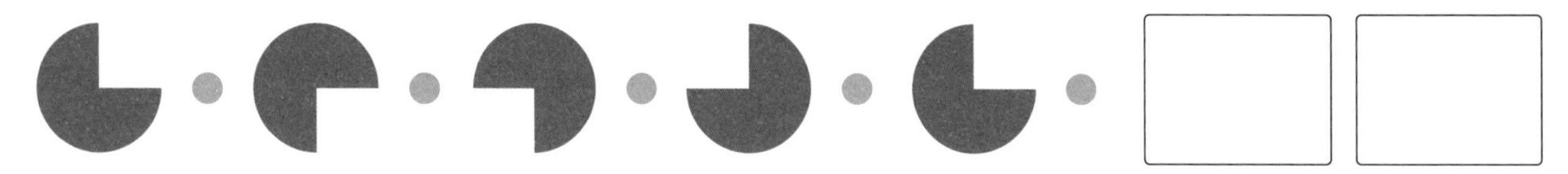

Describe the turn of the blue shape in this pattern.

____

Circle a statement to show how confident you feel about position and direction.

I am confident and could teach someone else.	I think I understand but I need practice.	I don't understand and need help.

Have a think about all the work you've done this term. What went well? What do you still need to practise?

I am confident with ______________________________.

I will practise ______________________________.